kidsource

super songs for church and school
compiled by **Capt. Alan Price, CA**

We hope you enjoy the music in this book. Further copies are available from your local music shop or Christian bookshop.

In case of difficulty, please contact the publisher direct by writing to:

The Sales Department
KEVIN MAYHEW LTD
Buxhall
Stowmarket
Suffolk IP14 3DJ

Phone 01449 737978
Fax 01449 737834
E-mail info@kevinmayhewltd.com

Please ask for our complete catalogue of outstanding Church Music.

First published in Great Britain in 1999 by Kevin Mayhew Ltd.

Compilation © Copyright 1999 Kevin Mayhew Ltd.

The right of Capt. Alan Price to be identified as the compiler of this work has been asserted by him in accordance with the Copyright, Designs and Patents Act 1988.

Full Music ISBN 1 84003 310 X
ISMN M 57004 506 8
Catalogue No: 1470154

Words Only ISBN 1 84003 311 8
Catalogue No: 1470151

1 2 3 4 5 6 7 8 9

Cover design by Jonathan Stroulger

Music Editor and Setter: Chris Hinkins
Assistant Editor: Kate Gallaher

Printed and bound in Great Britain

Foreword

Christ's message in all its richness must live in your hearts. Teach and instruct each other with all wisdom. Sing psalms, hymns and sacred songs; sing to God with thanksgiving in your hearts.

Colossians 3:16

Graham Kendrick started his preface in **the source**, the companion publication to this, with the same verse of scripture. It is with the same intent that we are pleased to introduce you to **kidsource**, this new collection of Christian songs with youngsters in mind.

Someone once said something like this: 'I don't mind the theology, as long as I can write the hymns'. The speaker was referring to the fact that many Christians seem to learn their theology from what they sing, rather than from any other source. For better or worse, it is the hymns and songs learnt in childhood that form the basis of faith for many.

Recent years have seen an 'explosion' of new music as much for children as for adults, yet in many churches the diet of music consists mainly of the hymns and songs of yesteryear. As good as many of them are, God has given so many new musical expressions of worship, which are much more relevant to this generation of children. There have been other collections, but, as with **the source**, we have sought to bring together as wide a range of songs as possible. There were many from which we had to choose, and often the choice was difficult.

Songs for children may be simpler and may have a high 'fun' content, but it is our conviction that whatever theological content they have should be good and biblically sound. We have sought to include hymns and songs that are primarily child-friendly, with good, memorable tunes, and words that express the Christian faith in terms that children can 'own'. There are one or two songs with an occasional grammatical 'slip-up', but they are still included because they are already popular with children and their leaders. There are also those that some might term 'adult' worship songs, but these have been included as those proven to be as accessible to children as to adults in their expression of faith and worship. It is also our belief that many adults will also find these 'children's' songs to be singable without any 'cringe-factor', thus being a collection providing a good resource for all-age worship.

Music is a major part of life, especially for children. Apart from the almost constant 'background music' surrounding them, the educational value of music is well known as a means of reinforcing teaching. However, music is also a vital means of expressing response to God and his message. Thus **kidsource** has songs suitable for reinforcing biblical teaching on a wide range of topics, and also those songs which will enable children to express their worship and adoration and their desire to follow the Friend and Saviour, Jesus Christ.

CAPT. ALAN PRICE, CA
Compiler

JONATHAN BUGDEN
Adviser

1 2 - 4 - 6 - 8, come and join the dance
(2 - 4 - 6 - 8 hoe-down!)

He'll mul – ti – ply your bles-sings and take your blues a-way. His love heals our di – vi-sions and adds va – lue to each day. sus!

CODA

Words and Music: Paul Crouch and David Mudie arr. Donald Thomson

2 5 0 0 0 + hungry folk

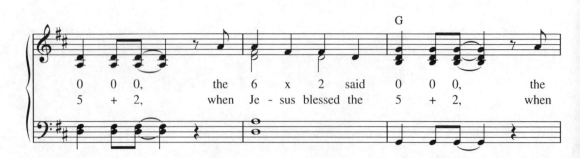

Words and Music: Ian Smale

3 Abba, Father, let me be

4 All heaven declares

Majestically

1. All heav'n de-clares the glo-ry of the ri-sen Lord.

Who can com-pare with the beau-ty of the Lord?

For e-ver he will be the Lamb up-on the throne.

I glad-ly bow the knee and wor-ship him a-lone.

2. I will proclaim
the glory of the risen Lord.
Who once was slain
to reconcile us to God.
For ever you will be
the Lamb upon the throne.
I gladly bow the knee
and worship you alone.

Words and Music: Noel and Tricia Richards

5 All I once held dear
(Knowing you)

1. All I once held dear, built my life up - on, all this

world re - veres, and wars to own, all I once thought gain I have

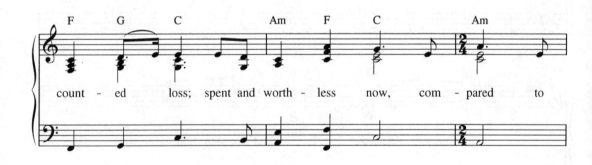

count - ed loss; spent and worth - less now, com - pared to

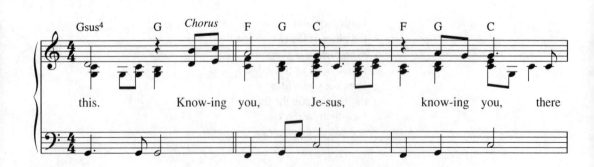

this. Know-ing you, Je-sus, know-ing you, there

is   no great-er   thing.   You're my all, you're the best, you're my

to repeat

joy, my right-eous-ness,   and I   love you, Lord.   2. Now my

last time

love you, Lord,   love you, Lord.

2. Now my heart's desire
   is to know you more,
   to be found in you
   and known as yours.
   To possess by faith
   what I could not earn,
   all-surpassing gift
   of righteousness.

3. Oh, to know the pow'r
   of your risen life,
   and to know you in
   your sufferings.
   To become like you
   in your death, my Lord,
   so with you to live
   and never die.

Words and Music: Graham Kendrick

6 All of my heart

Words and Music: Doug Marks-Smircich
© Copyright Right on the Mark Music. Copyright control.

7 All the creatures

1. All the crea-tures of the earth will de-clare that you are King. Ev-'ry wo-man, man and child con-fess you Lord of ev-'ry-thing. All cre-a-tion with one voice, ev'ry ga-la-xy and star, in a-do-ra-tion will pro-claim what a ho-ly God you are.

2. Ev'ry person will bow down,
   ev'ry eye will see your face.
   When your glory fills the sky,
   you will be seen in ev'ry place.
   All the people of the world,
   ev'rybody near and far,
   in adoration will proclaim
   what a holy God you are.

Words and Music: Paul Crouch and David Mudie arr. Donald Thomson

© Copyright 1997 Daybreak Music Ltd, Silverdale Road, Eastbourne,
East Sussex, BN20 7AB, UK. Used by permission.

8 All things bright and beautiful

TUNE 1: ROYAL OAK 76 76 and Refrain

2. The purple-headed mountain,
   the river running by,
   the sunset and the morning
   that brightens up the sky.

3. The cold wind in the winter,
   the pleasant summer sun,
   the ripe fruits in the garden,
   he made them ev'ry one.

4. He gave us eyes to see them,
   and lips that we may tell
   how great is God almighty,
   who has made all things well.

TUNE 2: ALL THINGS BRIGHT AND BEAUTIFUL 76 76 and Refrain

Words: Cecil Frances Alexander
Music: Tune 1 - traditional English melody arr. Adrian Vernon Fish
Tune 2 - William Henry Monk

9 Amazing grace

AMAZING GRACE CM

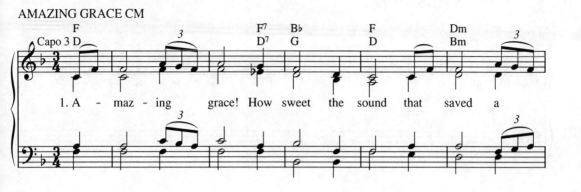

1. A - maz - ing grace! How sweet the sound that saved a

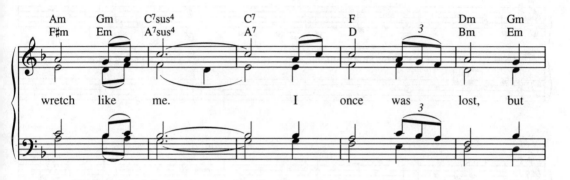

wretch like me. I once was lost, but

now I'm found; was blind, but now I see.

2. 'Twas grace that taught my heart to fear,
   and grace my fears relieved.
   How precious did that grace appear
   the hour I first believed.

3. Through many dangers, toils and snares
   I have already come.
   'Tis grace that brought me safe thus far,
   and grace will lead me home.

4. The Lord has promised good to me,
   his word my hope secures;
   he will my shield and portion be
   as long as life endures.

5. When we've been there a thousand years,
   bright shining as the sun,
   we've no less days to sing God's praise
   than when we first begun.

Words: John Newton alt.
Music: American folk melody arr. Richard Lloyd

10 A million stars are in the sky
(He is so great)

2. Great King of kings, he reigns on high,
   ruler of earth, and sea and sky.
   A tiny bird falls from a tree,
   God sees it all, and he knows me.

Words and Music: Karen Porter arr. Donald Thomson

11 And God said

2. And God said the grass should grow,
   the trees bear fruits, the winds should blow;
   and God said the streams should flow,
   and it was so, was so.

12 As for me and my house

As for me and my house, as for me and my fa - mi - ly, as for me and my child-ren, we will serve the Lord.

we will serve the Lord. In this fa - mi - ly, we're gon-na do things pro - per - ly, read God's word ev - 'ry day and then we'll try to pray; al-though we get it wrong, we will still car - ry on, make Je - sus num-ber one in this place. In this place we're gon-na say grace.

Words and Music: Jim Bailey

13 As we share bread in the family of God
(Communion song)

2. As we share wine in the fam'ly of God,
   we think of Jesus, God's Son.
   Rose from the dead in victory and pow'r.
   We adore you and worship you now.

Words and Music: Paul Crouch and David Mudie arr. Donald Thomson
© Copyright 1997 Daybreak Music Ltd, Silverdale Road, Eastbourne,
East Sussex, BN20 7AB, UK. Used by permission.

14 As with gladness men of old

1. As with glad-ness men of old did the guid-ing
star be-hold, as with joy they hailed its light,
lead-ing on-ward, beam-ing bright. So, most gra-cious God, may we
e-ver-more be led to thee. thee.

2. As with joyful steps they sped
   to that lowly manger-bed,
   there to bend the knee before
   him whom heav'n and earth adore.

3. As they offered gifts most rare,
   at that manger rude and bare,
   so may we with holy joy
   pure and free from sin's alloy.

4. Holy Jesu, ev'ry day
   keep us in the narrow way,
   and when earthly things are past
   save our ransomed souls at last.

Words: William Chatterton Dix alt. Roger Jones
Music: Roger Jones arr. Donald Thomson

15 Away in a manger

CRADLE SONG 11 11 11 11

2. The cattle are lowing, the baby awakes,
   but little Lord Jesus no crying he makes.
   I love thee, Lord Jesus! Look down from the sky,
   and stay by my side until morning is nigh.

3. Be near me, Lord Jesus; I ask thee to stay
   close by me for ever, and love me, I pray.
   Bless all the dear children in thy tender care,
   and fit us for heaven, to live with thee there.

Words: William James Kirkpatrick
Music: William James Kirkpatrick arr. Richard Lloyd
This arrangement © Copyright 1996 Kevin Mayhew Ltd.

16 A wiggly, waggly worm
(The wiggly waggly song)

A wig - gly, wag - gly worm, a slip - p'ry, sli - my slug, a cree - py, craw - ly, buz - zy thing, a tick - ly, wick - ly bug; of all the things to be, I'm hap - py that I'm me. Thank you, Lord, I'm hap - py that I'm me. I'm hap - py that I'm me, hap - py that I'm me. There's

no one else in all the world that I would ra-ther be. A wig-gly, wag-gly worm, a slip-p'ry, sli-my slug, a cree-py, craw-ly, buz-zy thing, a tick-ly, wick-ly bug.

2. A prickly porcupine, a clumsy kangaroo,
   a croaky frog, a hairy hog, a monkey in a zoo;
   of all the things to be, I'm happy that I'm me.
   Thank you, Lord, I'm happy that I'm me.
   I'm happy that I'm me, happy that I'm me.
   There's no one else in all the world that I would rather be.
   A prickly porcupine, a clumsy kangaroo,
   a croaky frog, a hairy hog, a monkey in a zoo.

Words and Music: Paul Field

17 Be bold, be strong

Words and Music: Morris Chapman

18 Because of who he is

1. Be-cause of who he is, be-cause of who he is, be-cause of all he's done, be-cause of all he's done, be-cause of all his love for us, we wor-ship the Three in One.

2. We have come to God the Father,
   we have come to God the Father,
   in the name of God the Son,
   in the name of God the Son,
   by the power of the Spirit,
   we worship the Three in One.

3. Because of who you are,
   because of who you are,
   because of all you've done,
   because of all you've done,
   because of all your love for us,
   we worship the Three in One.

Words and Music: Capt. Alan Price, CA

© Copyright 1994 Daybreak Music Ltd, Silverdale Road, Eastbourne,
East Sussex, BN20 7AB, UK. Used by permission.

19 Be still, for the presence of the Lord

Reverently

Be still, for the pre-sence of the Lord, the Ho - ly One is here.

Come, bow be - fore him now, with re - ver - ence and fear.

In him no sin is found, we stand on ho - ly ground.

Be still, for the pre-sence of the Lord, the Ho - ly One is here.

2. Be still, for the glory of the Lord is shining all around;
   he burns with holy fire, with splendour he is crowned.
   How awesome is the sight, our radiant King of light!
   Be still, for the glory of the Lord is shining all around.

3. Be still, for the power of the Lord is moving in this place;
   he comes to cleanse and heal, to minister his grace.
   No work too hard for him, in faith receive from him.
   Be still, for the power of the Lord is moving in this place.

Words and Music: David J. Evans

20 Be the centre of my life

Slowly

1. Be the cen-tre of my life, Lord Je-sus, be the cen-tre of my life, I pray; be my Sa-viour to for-give me, be my friend to be with me, be the cen-tre of my life to-day!

2. Let the power of your presence, Lord Jesus,
   from the centre of my life shine through;
   Oh, let ev'rybody know it,
   I really want to show it,
   that the centre of my life is you!

Words and Music: Capt. Alan Price, CA

© Copyright 1990 Daybreak Music Ltd, Silverdale Road, Eastbourne,
East Sussex, BN20 7AB, UK. Used by permission.

21 Calling on the Spirit

Calling on the Spirit (calling on the Spirit), Holy Spirit (Holy Spirit), come down to us (come down to us) in fire and rain (in fire and rain). Fire brings us ho-li-ness (fire brings us ho-li-ness), pu-ri-ty and pas-sion (pu-ri-ty and pas-sion), rain re-vives us (rain re-vives us), gives us hope a-gain.

Words and Music: Judy Bailey arr. Donald Thomson

22 Can we love one another

if some-times it's hard. Can we can and we will! e-ven

if some - times we fail and let him down. Yes, we

can and we will! yes, we can and we will! e - ven if some - times we

fail. Can we fail (God will help us). We will love one a-no-ther just like

Je - sus has loved us, and we will do what he com - mands!

Words and Music: Capt. Alan Price, CA

23 Can you count the stars

1. Can you count the stars shin-ing in the sky? Can you hold the moon-light in your hand? Can you stop the waves roll-ing on the shore? Or find the place where rain-bows meet the land?

Chorus I've got a friend who knows how all these things are done. Je-sus, Lord of all, God's on-ly Son.

2. Up in outer space, planets spinning round,
   millions more than we can ever see.
   It's hard to understand how God, who made it all,
   still cares about someone like you and me.

Words and Music: Paul Field
© Copyright 1991 Daybreak Music Ltd, Silverdale Road, Eastbourne,
East Sussex, BN20 7AB, UK. Used by permission.

24 Can you see what we have made
(Song for Christingle)

Verse F
Capo 3 D

1. Can you see what we have made for this ve - ry
2. Count the sea - sons as we sing, sum - mer, au - tumn,
5. There's a world I'm dream - ing of, where there's peace and

spe - cial day? An o - range for our pla - net home cir - cl - ing a -
win - ter, spring. Sing to God who sends the rain, mak - ing all things
joy and love. Light of Je - sus ev - 'ry - where, this is my Christ -

verse 1 *verses 2 & 5*

round the sun.
new a -
in - gle

(2.) gain.
(5.) prayer.

Chorus

Can - dle light, burn - ing bright, chase the dark - ness of the night.

(D.C. for verse 5)
Fine

Christ the light, light our way, live in - side our hearts to - day.

Words and Music: Graham Kendrick arr. Donald Thomson

25 Celebrate Jesus

Ce - le - brate Je - sus, ce - le - brate!

Ce - le - brate Je - sus, ce -

- le - brate!

- le - brate!

He is ri - sen, he is

Words and Music: Gary Oliver arr. Donald Thomson

26 Christmas, it's Christmas

Chorus
Chorus Christ - mas, it's Christ - mas, it's Christ-mas once a - gain.
last Chorus Christ - mas, it's Christ - mas, it's Christ-mas once a - gain.

The birth - day of Je - sus, born in Beth - le - hem.
We thank you, Lord Je - sus, that you came. A - men.

Verse
1. The Lord, who was that ti - ny ba - by,
2. The Lord, who was that ti - ny ba - by, grew

ex - ist - ed long be - fore the birth.
up and lived to show the Fa - ther's love.

verse 1

He laid a - side his heav'n-ly glo - - ry to be Je- sus,
He laid a - side his life to

Sa-viour of the earth! bring us back to God,

verse 2

raised to life, he's back in heav'n a - bove.

Words and Music: Capt. Alan Price, CA

27 Church is not a building

Words and Music: Robyn Barnett arr. Donald Thomson

28 C - L - A - P, clap my hands

C - L - A - P, clap my hands, J - U - M - P, jump! Yes, yes,

S - T - A - M - P my feet, for J - E - S - U - S!

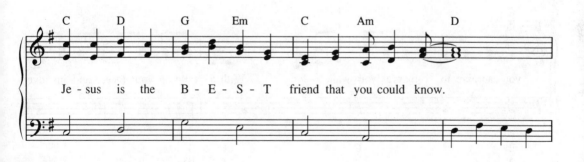

Je - sus is the B - E - S - T friend that you could know.

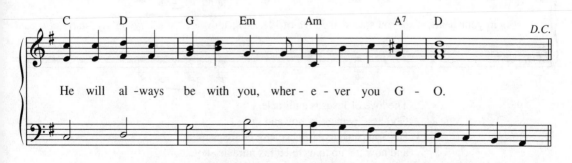

He will al - ways be with you, wher - e - ver you G - O.

Words and Music: Paul Crouch and David Mudie

29 Clap your hands

Chorus

Clap your hands, stomp your feet, spread the love of Je-sus to ev-'ry-one you meet. Oh! Clap your hands, stomp your feet, spread a lit-tle love a-round.

last time / to verses

Verse

1. The love of Je - sus is a sweet, sweet song, that you can give to o-thers as you walk a-long. With a smile on your face, and his love in your heart, you spread the love of Je-sus, now ev - 'ry-bo-dy start to

2. The love of Jesus is a miracle
   God has given ev'ry boy and girl.
   His Son came to earth because he loves us so,
   and now it's up to us to let his miracle show. Oh!

Words and Music: Tom Daniel, Bob Buzbee, Ernie Rettino and Debbie Kerner

30 Come along, everyone
(Let's worship God together)

Come a-long, ev-'ry-one, let's wor-ship God to-ge-ther. Come a-long, ev-'ry-one, let's wor-ship God to-ge-ther. Ev-'ry girl, ev-'ry boy, let's wor-ship God to-ge-ther. Praise, praise, praise, praise, praise to-ge-ther.

Words and Music: Yvonne Scott

© Copyright 1996 Daybreak Music Ltd, Silverdale Road, Eastbourne,
East Sussex, BN20 7AB, UK. Used by permission.

31 Come and join in the song
(He's alive!)

Chorus

Come and join in the song, Jesus Christ is Lord over all, and he lives to reign for evermore. The heavens applaud: 'He's alive! He's alive!' Lift your hearts and your voices, fill the earth with rejoicing for 1. he's ascended

to the skies, in hea-ven now he reigns. Lord of glo-ry,

Lord of life, he will re-turn a-gain!

CODA

'He's a-live!' He's a-live!'

2. Ev'ry knee shall bow to him,
   and ev'ryone confess:
   Jesus Christ is Lord and King,
   he's conquered sin and death!

3. Ev'ry nation, ev'ry tribe
   will glorify his name.
   All creation shall bow down
   and honour him with praise!

Words and Music: Mark and Helen Johnson arr. Donald Thomson

32 Come and sing

Verse

1. Come and sing, come and sing, come and sing to Je - sus now. Come and sing, come and sing, come and sing to Je - sus now.

Give him thanks for who he is, give him thanks for what he's done, come and sing.

Chorus

Je -

- sus won it all for us when he shed his blood on the cross.

Sin and death were swal-lowed up, they

don't have a hold on us now, that's the rea - son to sing.

1. 2.

2. Come and dance,

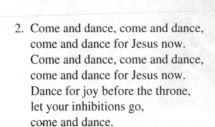

2. Come and dance, come and dance,
   come and dance for Jesus now.
   Come and dance, come and dance,
   come and dance for Jesus now.
   Dance for joy before the throne,
   let your inhibitions go,
   come and dance.

Words and Music: Mike Burn arr. Donald Thomson

33 Come, Jesus, come

Come, Jesus, come, touch my heart with a deep com-pas-sion. Lord, I want to see, I want to feel what you feel. Fill me with love, fill me with pow'r, send your Ho - ly Spi - rit. Come, Lord Je - sus, come.

Words and Music: Chris Jackson arr. Donald Thomson

34 Come on and celebrate
(Celebrate)

Come on and ce-le-brate his gift of love, we will

ce-le-brate the Son of God who loved us

and gave us life. We'll shout your

praise, O King, you give us joy no-thing else can bring,

we'll give to you our of - fer-ing in ce - le - bra - tion

praise. Come on and ce - le - brate,

ce - le - brate, ce - le - brate and sing,

1. ce - le - brate and sing to the King.

2. ce - le - brate and sing to the King.

Words and Music: Patricia Morgan and Dave Bankhead

35 Crackers and turkeys
(Somebody's birthday)

2. Ev'ryone's out shopping late ev'ry night,
   for candles and presents and Christmas tree lights.
   This is the Christmas that ev'ryone sees,
   but Christmas means more to me.

3. Christmas morning, the start of the day,
   there's presents to open and new games to play.
   This is the Christmas that ev'ryone sees,
   but Christmas means more to me.

Words and Music: Ian White arr. Donald Thomson

36 Dear Lord, my Father who's in heaven
(The Lord's Prayer)

Dear Lord, my Fa-ther who's in heav'n, ho-noured be your ho-ly name. May your king-dom come, may your will be done, here on earth as it is in heav'n. Dear Lord, please give us

Words and Music: Ian Smale

37 Do not worry

Words and Music: Doug Horley arr. Donald Thomson

38 Don't be afraid

2. Doesn't matter if you're big or small,
strong or insecure;
there's no easy way to live for God,
of that you can be sure.

Words and Music: Sammy Horner

39 Don't be an actor

Verse

1. You can dress up smart, you can dress up rough, you can
try to act big, you can try to act tough, but af - ter a while you'll have
had e - nough and what good would that do?

2. You can act happy when you're feeling down,
   you can put on a smile when your face wants to frown,
   you know it's no use trying to be a clown,
   just be the real 'you'.

Words and Music: Nick Harding arr. Donald Thomson

40 Don't build your house
(Sandy land)

Brightly

Don't build your house on the san - dy land,

don't build it too near the shore. Well, it

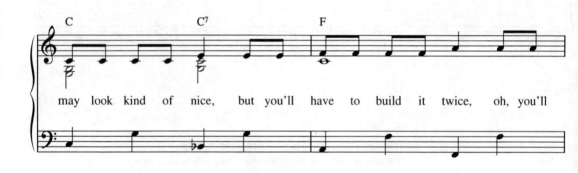

may look kind of nice, but you'll have to build it twice, oh, you'll

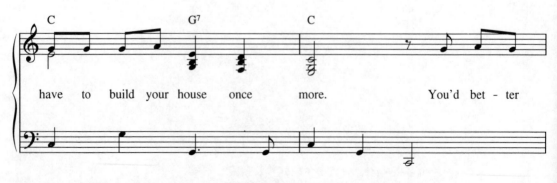

have to build your house once more. You'd bet - ter

build your house u - pon a rock, make a good foun - da - tion on a so - lid spot. Oh, the storms may come and go, but the peace of God you will know.

*This song can be sung as a round. Group 2 begins when Group 1 reaches *

Words and Music: Karen Lafferty

41 Don't know much about the ozone layer
(This is God's world)

Don't know much a-bout the o-zone lay-er, rain for-ests seem
miles a-way, but each of us can be a play-er, fight to save the world
God has made. This is God's world, this is God's
world, and you're a mem-ber of the hu-man race.
This is God's world, this is God's world,
let's try to make it a bet-ter place.

Words: Ralph Chambers
Music: Paul Field

42 Don't repay evil for evil

Don't re-pay e-vil for e-vil, don't snap back at those who say un-kind things a-bout you.

In-stead, pray, pray for God's help for them, for we are to be kind to o-thers. Pray, pray for God's help for them, and God will bless us for it.

Words and Music: Merrilyn Billing

43 Don't you worry about tomorrow
(Today)

Chorus

Don't you wor-ry a-bout to-mor - row, where you'll be or what you'll say. He'll take care of your to - mor - row if you just fol - low him to-day.

Verse

1. Where shall I go, what should I say, how do I know which is the way? Fac-ing the fu - ture, feel-ing a - fraid, time to re-mem - ber what Je - sus said.

2. When days are dark and nights are long,
   when times are hard and things go wrong,
   he'll never leave you, he won't let you down,
   he's there to lead you to solid ground.

Words and Music: Judy MacKenzie Dunn arr. Donald Thomson

44 Down in the jungle on a Saturday night
(The trouble)

Verse F (no 3rd)
Capo 3 D (no 3rd)

1. Down in the jun-gle on a Sa-tur-day night, all the a-ni-mals get to-ge - ther, to

talk a-bout the things that man has done to change the world for e - ver. The

G (no 3rd)
E (no 3rd)

won-ders of cre-a - tion die from greed and from pol-lu - tion, if

F (no 3rd)
D (no 3rd)

man's sup-posed to be so smart then where is the so-lu - tion?

Bb
G

F
D

Gm
Em

C
A

All things bright and beau - ti-ful, all crea-tures great and small, but the

2. When God made ev'ry living thing
he made the world for sharing.
He wants us all to get along
by loving and by caring.
A perfect earth for ev'ryone
that we should be enjoying,
so how is it that we have come
to spoiling and destroying?
All things wise and wonderful,
the Lord God made them all.
The trouble with man just seems to be
that he won't share at all.

Words and Music: Paul Field

45 Easter jubilation

With pace

Verse

1. Eas - ter ju - bi - la - tion fills the streets and towns, ce - le - bra - tions have be - gun. Hear the mu - sic and the dan - cing now, join the laugh - ter and the fun!

Chorus

Oh, raise a joy - ful shout! Clap your hands and dance, let your feel - ings out.

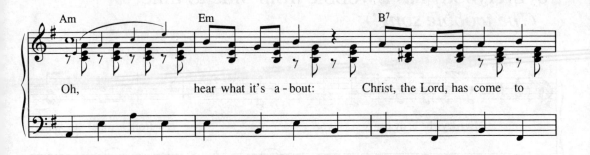

Oh,   hear what it's a-bout: Christ, the Lord, has come to

set us free.   set us free! Hoy!

2. Put aside your sorrows, wipe your tears away,
   for a better time will come.
   There's a promise of a better day,
   join the laughter and the fun!

3. La, la, la, la, la, etc,

4. Easter jubilation fills the streets and towns,
   celebrations have begun.
   Hear the music and the dancing now,
   join the laughter and the fun!

Words and Music: Mark and Helen Johnson

46 Everybody has a wobble from time to time
(The wobble song!)

Ev-'ry-bo-dy has a wob – ble from time to time, ev-'ry-bo-dy has some shake, rat-tle and roll in their li – ves. Ev-'ry-bo-dy has a wob – ble from time to time, ev-'ry-bo-dy has some shake, rat-tle and roll in their

Words and Music: Doug Horley arr. Donald Thomson

47 Every day with Jesus

shows me how my Chris-tian life can start.   Then as I get old-er,   just

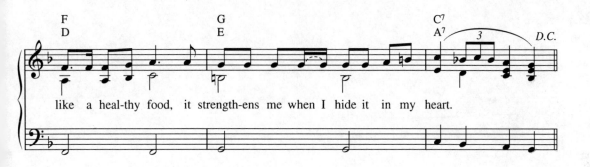

like a heal-thy food, it strength-ens me when I hide it in my heart.

2. I realise the Bible is a book I need to read,
   and ev'ry page I read I know is true.
   For God has breathed upon his book to help me ev'ry day,
   and show me what's his plan for me to do.

3. I realise the Bible is a book I need to read,
   the more I read the more I'm going to know,
   about the things of importance and how my life should be,
   it's what a Christian needs to make things grow.

Words and Music: Ian Smale

48 Everywhere he walks with me

2. Put to death whatever is sin,
   rid yourselves of all these things.
   You have been renewed in the Lord,
   and he is all, and is in all.

3. Let his peace now rule in your hearts.
   Let his Word be rich in you.
   Sing psalms and hymns with thanks to God,
   praise him in all that you do.

Words and Music: Ian White

49 Far and near
(Say it loud)

Verse

A   D   A

1. Far and near   hear the call,   wor - ship
    wide   is the love   hea - ven

E   D   A   D

him,   Lord of all;   fa - mi - lies   of na - tions,
sent   from a - bove;   God's own Son,   for sin - ners

A   E   D   **1.** A

come,   ce - le - brate   what God has done.   2. Deep and
died,   rose a - gain –   he is a -

2, 3. A   *Chorus*   A   A⁷   D

live.   Say it loud,   say it strong,   tell the

world   what God has   done;   say it

loud,   praise his name,   let the earth re-joice –

for   the   Lord   reigns.

3. At   his   reigns,   the Lord   reigns.

3. At his name, let praise begin;
   oceans roar, nature sing,
   for he comes to judge the earth
   in righteousness and in his truth.

Words and Music: Graham Kendrick

50 Father God, I come to you

Fa-ther God, I come to you and won-der at your love, that you
knew me, and you cared for me be-fore the world was made; and I
stand and think and love to feel your love so deep in-side, and to
know for sure your love for me will ne-ver, e-ver fade.

to repeat C D.C.

last time
fade, and to know for sure your love for me will ne-ver, e-ver fade.

Words and Music: Capt. Alan Price, CA arr. Gillian Venton
© Copyright 1996 Daybreak Music Ltd, Silverdale Road, Eastbourne,
East Sussex, BN20 7AB, UK. Used by permission.

51 Father God, I know you love me so
(I'm so small)

2. Father God, I'm small but I love you so,
   Father God, I'm small but I'll follow you.
   Father God, I'm small but I love you so,
   Father God, I'm small but I'll follow you.

Words and Music: Yvonne Scott

© Copyright 1993 Daybreak Music Ltd, Silverdale Road, Eastbourne,
East Sussex, BN20 7AB, UK. Used by permission.

52 Father God, I wonder
(I will sing your praises)

Words and Music: Ian Smale

53 Father God, you love me

1. Fa-ther God, you love me and you know me in - side out. You
know the words that I will say be - fore I speak them out.
You are all a-round me, you hold me in your hand, your
love for me is more than I can e - ver un -der - stand.

2. Father God, from your love there is nowhere I can hide.
   If I go down into the depths or cross the ocean wide,
   there your love would find me, you'd take me in your hand.
   Your love for me is more than I can ever understand.

Words and Music: Paul Crouch and David Mudie

54 Father, I can call you Father

Fa - ther,   Fa - ther   to me.

2. Father, how I love you,
   Father, I will sing your praise,
   today, tomorrow and always,
   for you're my Father.

3. Father, I will serve you,
   Father, I will seek your face,
   today, tomorrow and always,
   you are my Father.

Words and Music: Danny Daniels

55 Father, I do adore you

Flowing

1. Fa-ther, I do a-dore you, wor-ship be-fore you, I love you, Lord.

Fine *Chorus* You have o-pened up my eyes to see such beau-ty in your face, a love that cared e-nough to set me free; and my heart is filled with won-der at the glo-ry of your grace, I'm so thank-ful, Lord, that now you live in me.

2. Jesus, I do adore you, . . .

3. Spirit, I do adore you, . . .

Words and Music: Judy Bailey and Dave Bankhead

56 Father, I thank you

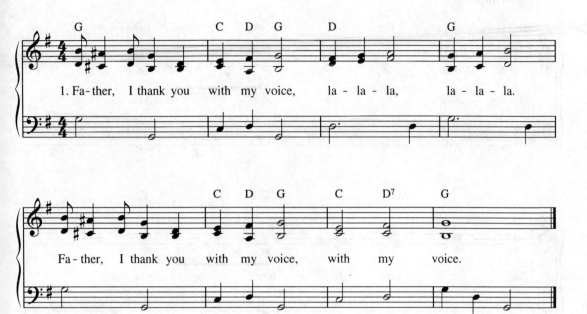

1.
(No actions)

2. Father, I thank you with my hands,
   with my hands, with my hands.
   Father, I thank you with my hands,
   with my hands.
(Each time the words 'with my hands' are sung, then clap hands)

3. Father, I thank you with my feet,
   with my feet, with my feet.
   Father, I thank you with my feet,
   with my feet.
(Each time the words 'with my feet' are sung, then jump or dance)

4. Father, I thank you with my voice,
   with my hands, with my feet.
   Father, I thank you with my voice,
   hands and feet.
('With my voice' – no action, 'with my hands' – clap,
'with my feet' – jump/dance)

Words and Music: Yvonne Scott

© Copyright 1993 Daybreak Music Ltd, Silverdale Road, Eastbourne,
East Sussex, BN20 7AB, UK. Used by permission.

57 Father, we adore you

This song may sung as a round, new voices entering at the start of each line.

2. Jesus, we adore you . . .

3. Spirit, we adore you . . .

Words and Music: Terrye Coelho

58 Father, your word

Fa - ther, your word is like a light in the dark - ness.

Fa - ther, your word is like a sharp, sharp sword.

Fa - ther, your word is like a stream in the de - sert. There's

no - thing that com - pares with the wis - dom of your word.

Words and Music: Paul Crouch and David Mudie

© Copyright 1990 Daybreak Music Ltd, Silverdale Road, Eastbourne,
East Sussex, BN20 7AB, UK. Used by permission.

59 Find the silence through the noise
(Give him your heart)

Words and Music: Paul Field

60 For ever I will live my life by faith
(Live my life by faith)

2. By faith I take God's hand,
   by faith I understand,
   by faith I am made pure,
   by faith I can be sure.

Words and Music: Nick Harding arr. Gillian Venton

61 For I'm building a people of power

Words and Music: Dave Richards

62 From heaven you came
(The Servant King)

1. From heav'n you came, help-less babe, en-tered our world, your glo-ry veiled; not to be served but to serve, and give your life that we might live. This is our God, the Ser-vant

2. There in the garden of tears,
   my heavy load he chose to bear;
   his heart with sorrow was torn.
   'Yet not my will but yours,' he said.

3. Come see his hands and his feet,
   the scars that speak of sacrifice,
   hands that flung stars into space,
   to cruel nails surrendered.

4. So let us learn how to serve,
   and in our lives enthrone him;
   each other's needs to prefer,
   for it is Christ we're serving.

Words and Music: Graham Kendrick arr. Donald Thomson

63 F - U - N - E - N - R - G?

1. F - U - N - E - N - R - G? Come and praise the Lord with me. O - I - C - Y - M - 2 - B filled with joy and vic - tor - E. F - U - N - E - N - R - G? S - V - F - Z - N - R - G. J - E - S - U - S for me, S - S - Y - I - M so 3.

(More slowly)
2. F - U - F - N - 10 - E bounce,
   & U - F - N - 10 - E go,
   come 2 J - E - S - U - S,
   E - L give U zap 2 glow.
   O - I - 8 - 2 - C - U sad,
   & I - 8 - 2 - C - U low,
   U - C - U - R - O - K 2 God,
   & E wants 2 C - U grow!

The Interpretation

1. *Have you any energy?*
   Come and praise the Lord with me.
   Oh, I see why I'm to be
   filled with joy and victory.
   Have you any energy?
   'Yes, we have the energy.'
   J - E - S - U - S for me,
   this is why I am so free.

2. *If you haven't any bounce,*
   and you haven't any go,
   come to J - E - S - U - S,
   he will give you zap to glow.
   Oh, I hate to see you sad,
   and I hate to see you low,
   you see you are O.K. to God,
   and he wants to see you grow.

Words and Music: Richard Hubbard

64 Get on board!
(Kingdom train)

To sing as a two-part round, 2nd voices begin when 1st voices reach ☐1

Words and Music: Capt. Alan Price, CA arr. Gillian Venton

65 Give me a heart of compassion
(Enable your servants)

1. Give me a heart of com-pas-sion, give me a hope for the lost. Give me a pas-sion for those who are bro-ken and down. Lord, I am rea-dy and will-ing to serve the weak and the young. Help me to put in-to ac-tion the words of this song.

And en - a - ble your ser - vants, en - a - ble your ser - vants to preach good news,

to preach good news. And en -

2. I'll sing the songs of salvation,
   boldly I'll speak out your word.
   I'll let them know by my life,
   I will show you are Lord.
   I'll tell them all about Jesus,
   I'll tell them all about you,
   I'm not ashamed of the gospel
   or what it can do.

3. We're moving forward together,
   as one voice boldly proclaim,
   the old and the young will be strong,
   and we'll lift up your name
   on to the streets to the people,
   ev'ry man, woman and child,
   and as we go you are with us,
   you've given your pow'r.

   You've enabled your servants . . .

Words and Music: Jim Bailey arr. Donald Thomson

66 Give me oil in my lamp

2. Give me joy in my heart, keep me singing.
   Give me joy in my heart, I pray.
   Give me joy in my heart, keep me singing,
   keep me singing till the break of day.

3. Give me love in my heart, keep me serving.
   Give me love in my heart, I pray.
   Give me love in my heart, keep me serving,
   keep me serving till the break of day.

4. Give me peace in my heart, keep me resting.
   Give me peace in my heart, I pray.
   Give me peace in my heart, keep me resting,
   keep me resting till the break of day.

Words: traditional
Music: traditional arr. John Ballantine

67 Gives! Gives! Gives!
(God is very great)

1. Gives! Gives! Gives! That's what God does. Gives! Gives! Gives! That's what God does each day. Great! Great! Great! God is ve - ry great.

2. Thanks! Thanks! Thanks!
   That's what we say.
   Thanks! Thanks! Thanks!
   That's what we say each day.
   Great! Great! Great!
   God is very great.

Words and Music: Yvonne Scott

68 Give thanks with a grateful heart

Give thanks with a grateful heart. Give thanks to the Ho - ly One. Give thanks be-cause he's gi - ven Je - sus Christ, his Son.

1, 3. Give Son. **2, 4.** And now let the weak say, 'I am strong', let the poor say, 'I am

rich', be-cause of what the Lord has done for

us. And now let the weak say, 'I am strong', let the

poor say, 'I am rich', be-cause of what the Lord has

done for us. Give us. Give thanks.

Words and Music: Henry Smith arr. Donald Thomson

69 Glory

Bright, joyful feel

Glo - ry, glo - ry in the high - est; glo - ry

to the Al - migh - ty; glo - ry to the Lamb of God, and

glo - ry to the liv - ing Word; glo - ry

Words and Music: Danny Daniels

70 God always has time for us

God always has time for us, he will always listen.
God always has time for us, time for ev-'ry one. He
cares for you and he cares for me, he isn't too bu-sy,
is he? No! He cares for you and he cares for me, he
isn't too bu-sy, is he? No! bu-sy for us!

Words and Music: Capt. Alan Price, CA arr. Gillian Venton

71 God has a perfect plan for me
(God's perfect plan)

1. God has a per-fect plan for me, God has a per-fect plan for me. Fol-low-ing Je-sus is where I want to be, God has a per-fect plan for me. He knows the end from the be-gin-ning, he sees the path I need to take. I have a part to play in God's a-maz-ing plan, so

last time to Coda

D.C. in verse 3

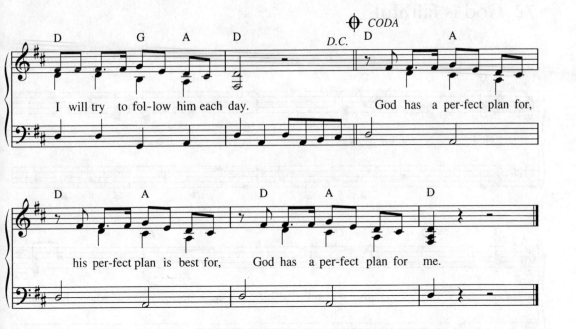

CODA

I will try to fol-low him each day. God has a per-fect plan for,

his per-fect plan is best for, God has a per-fect plan for me.

2. You have a perfect plan for me,
   you have a perfect plan for me.
   Following you, Lord, is where I want to be,
   you have a perfect plan for me.
   You know the end from the beginning,
   you see the path I need to take.
   I have a part to play in your amazing plan,
   so help me, Lord, to follow you each day.

3. God has a perfect plan for you,
   God has a perfect plan for you.
   To follow Jesus – that's what we want to do,
   God has a perfect plan for you.
   God has a perfect plan for me,
   God has a perfect plan for me.
   Following Jesus is where I want to be,
   God has a perfect plan for,
   his perfect plan is best for,
   God has a perfect plan for me.

Words and Music: Paul Crouch and David Mudie

72 God is faithful

God is faith - ful, he is the one.

God is faith - ful, he's the one who has called

us to share life with his Son, Je - sus

1. Christ our Lord. **2.** Christ our

Lord. Je - sus Christ our Lord.

Words and Music: Chris Jackson

73 God is good, God is great

God is good, God is great, he's the one who did cre-ate ev-'ry-thing that there is by his pow-er.

God is thing that there is by his po-wer.

1. Thank you, Lord, for the things I can see, thank you, thank you, Lord.

Thank you, Lord, for the sounds I can hear, thank you, thank you, Lord.

2. Thank you, Lord, for my family,
   thank you, thank you, Lord.
   Thank you, Lord, for all my friends,
   thank you, thank you, Lord.

3. Thank you, Lord, for the birds in the sky,
   thank you, thank you, Lord.
   Thank you, Lord, for the ants on the ground,
   thank you, thank you, Lord.

4. Thank you, Lord, for your love to me,
   thank you, thank you, Lord.
   Thank you, Lord, that you're always near,
   thank you, thank you, Lord.

Words and Music: Capt. Alan Price, CA

© Copyright 1994 Daybreak Music Ltd, Silverdale Road, Eastbourne,
East Sussex, BN20 7AB, UK. Used by permission.

74 God is good

Fast and rhythmic

God is good, we sing and shout it, God is good,

we ce - le - brate. God is good, no more we doubt it,

God is good, we know it's true.

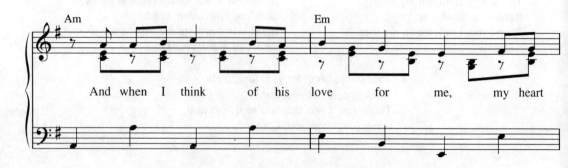

And when I think of his love for me, my heart

fills with praise and I feel like danc - ing.

For in his heart there is room for me and I

D.C. al Coda

run with arms op-en'd wide.

CODA

(shout)

we know it's true. Hey!

Words and Music: Graham Kendrick

75 God is here, God is here
(Almighty God is here)

God is here, God is here, Al - migh-ty God is here. Bow down be-

fore him in re - ve- rence and fear. God is here, God is here, Al -

migh-ty God is here, Al - migh - ty God is here. 1. It's

hard to i - ma - gine how it could e - ver be that the ma-ker of the

u-ni-verse is now here with me. I'll no long-er live in lone-li-ness, nor

fear the e - ne - my. Al - migh - ty God is here.

2. As I see my generation in sadness and in pain,
   I hear the fools say, 'There's no God', time and time again.
   But fools can never change the fact our God is here to reign.
   Almighty God is here.

3. So let's call together all the saints, their voices to proclaim
   that the Father, Son and Spirit will forever be the same,
   and the day will come when every knee shall bow at Jesus' name.
   Almighty God is here.

Words and Music: Ian Smale

76 God is here, God is present

With awe · Em · B7 · Em

God is here, God is pre-sent, God is mov - ing by his

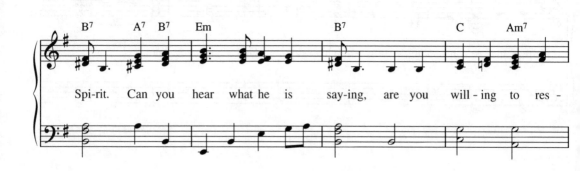

B7 · A7 · B7 · Em · B7 · C · Am7

Spi-rit. Can you hear what he is say-ing, are you will - ing to res -

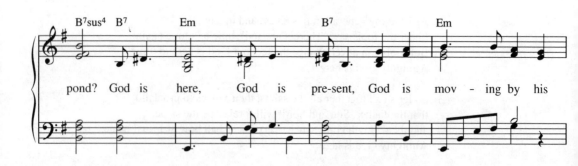

B7sus4 · B7 · Em · B7 · Em

pond? God is here, God is pre-sent, God is mov - ing by his

B7 · A7 · B7 · A7 · Am7

Spi - rit. Lord, I o - pen up my life to you, please

Words and Music: Ian Smale

77 God is our Father

Words and Music: Alex Simons and Freda Kimmey

78 God is so good

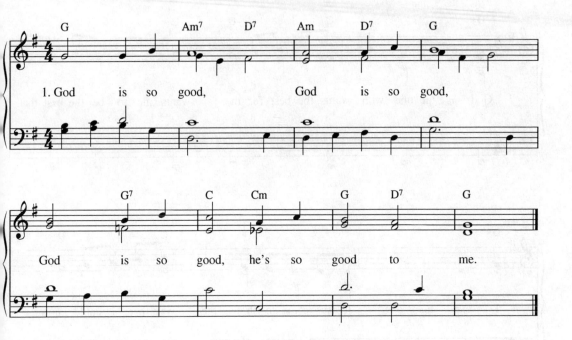

1. God is so good, God is so good, God is so good, he's so good to me.

2. He took my sin,
   he took my sin,
   he took my sin,
   he's so good to me.

3. Now I am free,
   now I am free,
   now I am free,
   he's so good to me.

4. God is so good,
   he took my sin,
   now I am free,
   he's so good to me.

79 God is the one

God is the one who wants the best for me, wants me to be the best that I can be. Je-sus came to show the way that I could know life in all its full-ness if to him I go. He for-gives my sin and fills me ev-'ry day with pow'r to live for Je-sus in all I do and say. There is

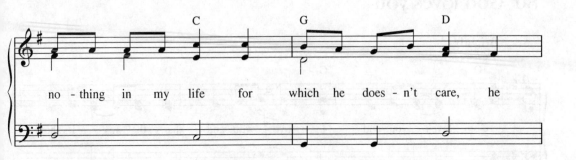

no - thing in my life for which he does - n't care, he

1, 2.

al - ways will be with me, all the time and ev - 'ry - where.

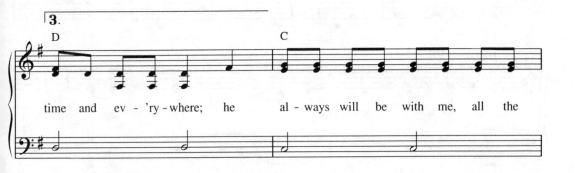

3.

time and ev - 'ry - where; he al - ways will be with me, all the

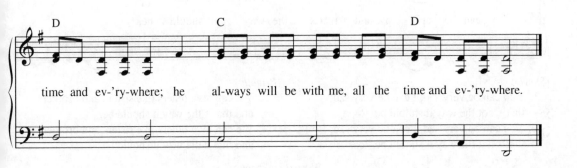

time and ev-'ry-where; he al-ways will be with me, all the time and ev-'ry-where.

Words and Music: Capt. Alan Price, CA

80 God loves you

Brightly

Chorus

God loves you, and I love you, and that's the way it should be.
God loves you, and I love you, and that's the way it should be.

Fine Verse

1. You can be hap-py, and I can be hap-py, and that's the way it should be. You can be hap-py, and I can be hap-py, and that's the way it should be.

(Slowly) Dm Gm
2. You can be very sad, I can be very sad;
Dm that's not the way it should be. A7
Dm You can be very sad, I can be very sad; Gm
that's not the way it should be, 'cos . . .

Dm A D

(Brightly)
3. We can love others like sisters and brothers;
and that's the way it should be.
We can love others like sisters and brothers;
and that's the way it should be.

Words: Unknown
Music: arr. Donald Thomson
This arrangement © Copyright 1999 Kevin Mayhew Ltd. Used by permission.

81 God loves you so much

1. God loves you so much, God wants you so much, God wants to tell you so much that he put it in a book for you. And it's the Bi - ble. Yes, it's the Bi - ble. Oh, it's the Bi - ble. Yes, he put it in a let-ter so we could know him bet-ter.

CODA
put it in a book for, put it in a book for, put it in a book for you.

2. He wants to know you so much,
   he wants to know you so much,
   God wants to tell you so much
   that he put it in a book for,
   put it in a book for,
   put it in a book for you.

Words and Music: Derek Llewellyn

82 God made a boomerang

With bounce

God made a boom-er-ang and called it love,
God made a boom-er-ang and called it love, God made a boom-er-ang and
called it love, and then he threw it a-way!

Verse

1. Love's like a boom-er-ang, that's what we've found, it
comes right back when you throw it a-round.

Some-thing we can share out, ne - ver seems to wear out,
love's like a boom - er - ang, let's throw it a - round.

2. Love's like a boomerang, that's what God planned,
   but it's no use if it stays in your hand.
   Gotta send it spinning
   for a new beginning,
   love's like a boomerang, let's throw it around.

3. Love's like a boomerang, goes with a swing,
   now ev'rybody can have a good fling.
   Families and nations
   join the celebrations,
   love's like a boomerang, let's throw it around.

Words: Michael Forster
Music: Christopher Tambling

83 God never gives up

Chorus

God ne - ver gives up, he ne - ver gives up, he
ne - ver gives up on me, no sir! God ne - ver gives up, he
ne - ver gives up, he ne - ver will cease to care!

verse 1

1. I know I don't de - serve the love that Je - sus has for me. He
died that I could be for - giv'n and be all I could be!

verses 2-4

Em   Am   F   G   C

2. E - ven when I for - get him   and hard - ly e - ver pray,   the
3. E - ven when I de - ny him,   pre - tend that I don't care,   the
4. E - ven when I might hurt him   with care - less words and deeds,

Em   Am   D7   verses 2-3   G   D.C.

Spi - rit of Je - sus deep in - side as - sures me when I say:
Spi - rit of Je - sus deep in - side re - minds me he's still there!
Fa - ther God still will love me,   and care for all my

verse 4

G   Bridge   C   F

needs! So I'll ne - ver give up,   try not to give up,   try

C   G   G7   C

not to give up on him,   please God! His Spi - rit with - in will

F   C   G   D.C.

help me to win   when I'm temp - ted to give up on him!

Words and Music: Capt. Alan Price, CA

84 God's love is deeper
(Deeper, wider, higher)

1. God's love is dee-per than the deep-est o-cean, God's love is
wi-der than the wi-dest sea, God's love is high-er than the high-est moun-tain,
dee-per, wi-der, high-er is God's love to me. Dee-per, wi-der, high-er,
dee-per, wi-der, high-er, dee-per, wi-der, high-er is God to me.

2. God's grace is deeper than . . .

3. God's joy is deeper than . . .

4. God's peace is deeper than . . .

Words and Music: Iain Craig

© Copyright 1993 Daybreak Music Ltd, Silverdale Road, Eastbourne,
East Sussex, BN20 7AB, UK. Used by permission.

85 God's not dead

Left hand octaves are optional

Words: Unknown alt. G. Leavers and P. J. Horrobin
Music: arr. Donald Thomson

86 God's people

God's peo-ple aren't su-per-brave su-per-he-roes, they

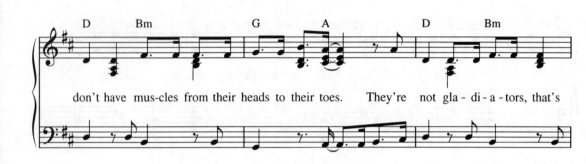

don't have mus-cles from their heads to their toes. They're not gla-di-a-tors, that's

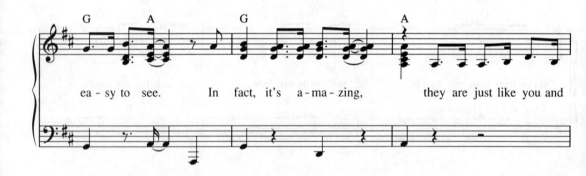

ea-sy to see. In fact, it's a-ma-zing, they are just like you and

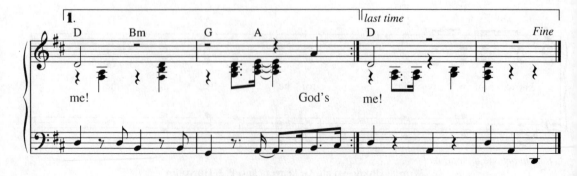

1.
me!   God's   me!

me! Some - times scared,

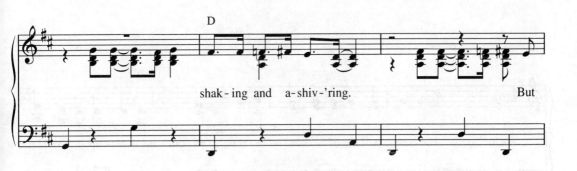

shak - ing and a - shiv -'ring. But

let's re - a - lise we've got God on our side, and he can do

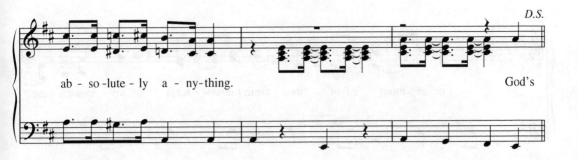

D.S.

ab - so - lute - ly a - ny - thing. God's

Words and Music: John Hardwick

87 God's rubbered out all my mistakes
(The stationery song)

With a calypso feel

1. God's rub-bered out all my mis-takes, he's e-rased all my

sin. He's the ru-ler of cre - a-tion, no one mea-sures up to him.

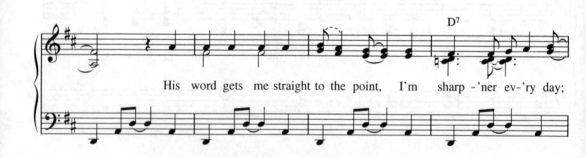

His word gets me straight to the point, I'm sharp -'ner ev-'ry day;

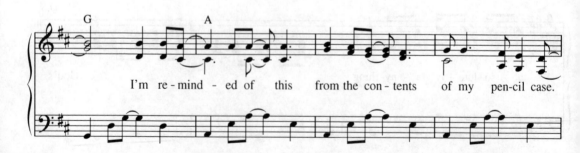

I'm re-mind - ed of this from the con - tents of my pen-cil case.

2. I am never stationery,
   always moving on.
   I felt the tip of his love,
   now I know that God's right on.
   His love's compassed about me,
   I'm stapled to his grace;
   I'm reminded of this from the contents
   of my pencil case.

Words and Music: Jim Bailey arr. Donald Thomson

88 God trains all his children
(The vine)

God trains all his chil-dren as a gard-'ner trains a vine, wa-ter-ing and prun-ing so it grows in-to the sun-shine. And in time he is re-war-ded when he sees fruit on the tree. So our Fa-ther loves to see the Spi-rit's fruit in you and me. Love, joy, peace, pa-tience, good-ness, kind-ness, faith-ful-ness, gen-tle-ness and self-con-trol.

Words and Music: Paul Crouch and David Mudie

89 God, you can use me

2. God, you can use me,
   God, you can use me,
   that the world may see the Lord Jesus,
   God, you can use me.

3. God, you can use me,
   God, you can use me,
   that the world may love the Lord Jesus,
   God, you can use me.

4. God, you can use us,
   God, you can use us,
   that the world may praise the Lord Jesus,
   God, you can use us.

Words and Music: Graeme Young

90 Go, go, go

Brightly

1. Go, go, go in-to the world.
Go, go, go in-to the world.
Go, go, go in-to the world. Tell your mum and dad the good news that you've had; Je - sus Christ is Lord.

2. Go, go, go into the world.
Go, go, go into the world.
Go, go, go into the world.
Go and tell the rest
Jesus is the best;
tell every boy and girl.

Words and Music: Jim Bailey

91 Good or bad

Good or bad, right or wrong, we have to choose each day.

Truth or lie, share or keep, ig-nore the rules or o-bey.

Je-sus is the one we need to help us choose the right way;

Je-sus, you're the one we need, help us, Lord, to-day!

Words and Music: Capt. Alan Price, CA

92 Grace is

1. Grace is when God gives us the things we don't de - serve.
Grace is when God gives us the things we don't de - serve. He
does it be-cause he loves us, he does it be-cause he loves us.
Grace is when God gives us the things we don't de - serve.

2. Mercy is when God does not
give us what we deserve.
Mercy is when God does not
give us what we deserve.
He does it because he loves us,
he does it because he loves us.
Mercy is when God does not
give us what we deserve.

Words and Music: Paul Crouch and David Mudie

93 Hands, hands, fingers, thumbs

Words and Music: Doug Horley arr. Donald Thomson

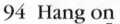

94 Hang on

1. Hang on, stand still, stay put, hold tight; wait for the Spi-rit of God.

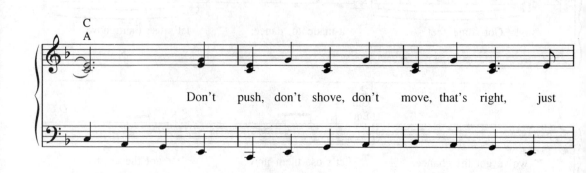

Don't push, don't shove, don't move, that's right, just

wait for the Spi-rit of God. Hang For you will re-ceive the

pow-er of God. You will re-ceive the pow-er of God.

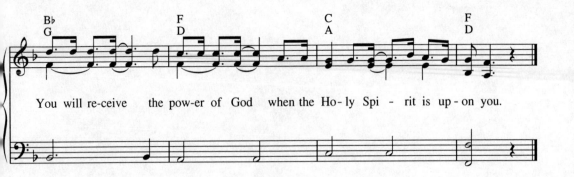

You will re-ceive the pow-er of God when the Ho- ly Spi - rit is up - on you.

2. Let go, launch out,
   press on, don't fight;
   be filled with the Spirit of God.
   Move on, make way,
   step out, that's right;
   be filled with the Spirit of God.
   (Repeat)

For you have received the power of God,
you have received the power of God.
You have received the power of God
now the Holy Spirit lives within you.

Words and Music: Richard Hubbard arr. Donald Thomson

95 Harvest time

1. Har-vest time is the time when all the crops are high, all the food must be cut and stored up in the dry. Har-vest time – see the fruit, the maize and wheat, all the food for us to eat, it must be har-vest time.

2. Harvest time, we have always got so much to eat,
   but for some just a little is a real feast.
   Harvest time – let's remember all the poor,
   and let's try to give them more
   after this harvest time.

3. Harvest time is the time when we should all thank God
   for each grain, ev'ry apple and the green pea pod.
   Harvest time – see the fruit, the maize and wheat,
   so much food for us to eat.
   Thank God for harvest time.

Words and Music: Nick Harding arr. Donald Thomson

96 Have we made our God too small?

Have we made our God too small, too small? Have we made our God too small? He made the hea-vens and earth and he reigns on high, yet he's got the time for you and I. Have we you and I.

See the glo-ry of God light up the sky, as the

Words and Music: Doug Horley

97 Have you got an appetite?

1. Have you got an ap-pe-tite? Do you eat what is right? Are you feed-ing on the word of God? Are you fat or are you thin? Are you real-ly full with-in? Do you find your strength in him or are you starv-ing?

Chorus
You and me, all should be ex-er-cis-ing

re-gu-lar-ly, stand-ing strong   all day long,   giv-ing God the   glo - ry.

Feed-ing on the   liv-ing Bread, not eat-ing crumbs but loaves in-stead;   stand-ing strong-er,

liv-ing   long-er,   giv-ing God the   glo - ry,   giv-ing God the   glo - ry.

last time

2. If it's milk or meat you need,
   why not have a slap-up feed,
   and stop looking like a weed and start to grow?
   Take the full-of-fitness food,
   taste and see that God is good,
   come on, feed on what you should and be healthy.

Words and Music: Mick Gisbey

98 Have you heard

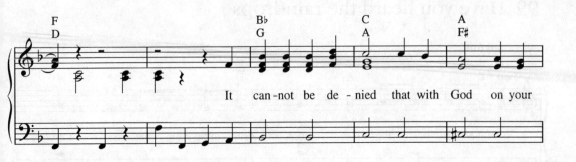

It can-not be de - nied that with God on your

side, it's a - ma -zing what the Lord can do.

2 & 3. Have you

2. Have you heard about the boy in the lions' den?
   Punished by the king for praying to the Lord and then
   God's angel came to save his servant from the grave.
   Daniel was on the side of God.

3. Have you heard about the boy with the sling and the stone?
   How he fought a ten-foot giant all alone.
   God chose him to be king, a most unusual thing.
   David was on the side of God.

Words: Ralph Chambers
Music: Paul Field

99 Have you heard the raindrops

2. There's a busy worker digging in the desert,
   digging with a spade that flashes in the sun;
   soon there will be water rising in the well-shaft,
   spilling from the bucket as it comes.

3. Nobody can live who hasn't any water,
   when the land is dry, then nothing much grows;
   Jesus gives us life if we drink the living water,
   sing it so that everybody knows.

Words and Music: Christian Strover
© Copyright Christian Strover/Jubilate Hymns, 4 Thorne Park Road,
Chelston, Torquay, TQ2 6RX, UK. Used by permission.

100 Have you seen the pussycat

Simply

Verse F ... Gm ... C
Capo 3 D ... Em ... A

1. Have you seen the pus-sy-cat sit-ting on the wall?
   Have you seen the li-on stalk-ing round his prey?

Have you heard his beau-ti-ful purr? *(purr)*
Have you heard his ter-ri-ble roar? *(roar)*

Chorus

One so big, one so small, our heav'n-ly Fa-ther cares for them all;

one so big, one so small, our heav'n-ly Fa-ther cares.

2. Have you seen the children coming home from school?
   Have you heard them shout 'Hurray!' *(Hurray!)*
   Have you seen the grown-ups coming home from work,
   saying, 'What a horrible day!' *(What a horrible day!)*

   Some so big, . . .

Words and Music: P. A. Taylor

101 Heaven is a wonderful place

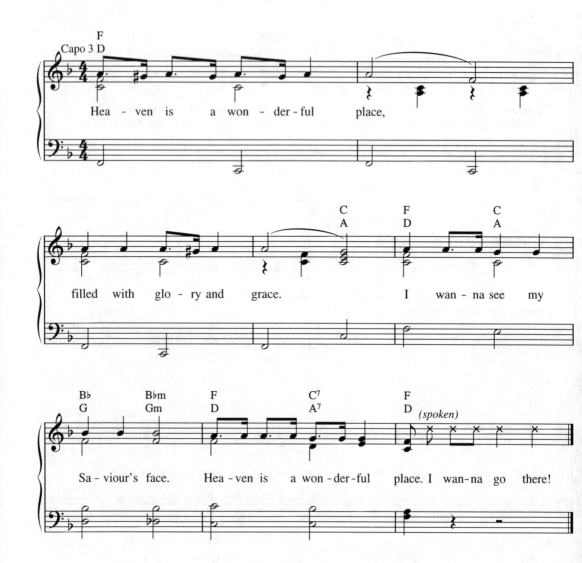

Hea - ven is a won - der - ful place,
filled with glo - ry and grace. I wan - na see my
Sa - viour's face. Hea - ven is a won - der - ful place. I wan-na go there!

102 He is the King of kings
(Jesus is his name)

1. All my friends at school say I'm a fool
   because I trust in him ev'ry day,
   and I hold on to what I know is true,
   he is the light, the truth, the way.

2. When I feel far from him, he is still there.
   He draws so close as I talk to him in prayer.
   He is my Lord and yet he is a king,
   and Jesus is his name.

Words and Music: Iain Craig

© Copyright 1995 Daybreak Music Ltd, Silverdale Road, Eastbourne,
East Sussex, BN20 7AB, UK. Used by permission.

103 He is the Lord
(Show your power)

Strong and rhythmic

1. He is the Lord, and he reigns on high; he is the Lord.

Spoke in-to the dark-ness, cre-a-ted the light.

He is the Lord. Who is like un-to him, ne-ver-

end-ing in days; he is the Lord. And

Words and Music: Kevin Prosch

104 Here I am, Lord

105 Here I am, ready to go

Words: Merete Åsebøe-Blindheim trans. by Capt. Alan Price, CA
Music: Merete Åsebøe-Blindheim arr. Donald Thomson

106 Here's a song

Breezy pace, not too fast

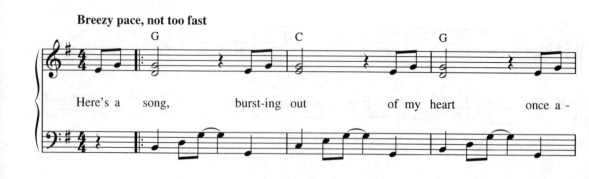

Here's a song, burst-ing out of my heart once a-

gain. Je - sus Christ, you're so good that I can't keep it

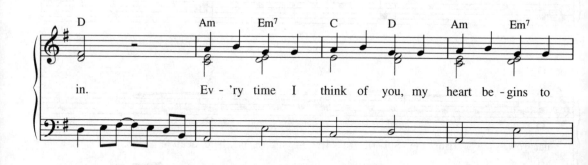

in. Ev - 'ry time I think of you, my heart be - gins to

sing. Lis-ten, Lord, to the songs we sing, la la la,

Move into a 'Na na na' version of the 'Here we go' football chant,
picking up the song once more at 'Listen, Lord . . .'

Words and Music: Matt Redman and Capt. Alan Price, CA arr. Donald Thomson

107 Higher, higher
(Cast your burdens)

In a calypso style

Words and Music: Issac Balinda arr. Stuart Townend

108 Higher than the highest mountain
(Talkin' 'bout Jesus)

With bounce

2. We're sing - in' 'bout *etc.*
3. We're whisp - 'rin' 'bout *etc.*
4. We're shout - in' 'bout *etc.*

Words and Music: Mark and Helen Johnson

109 Ho ho ho hosanna

110 Hold on to the promises of God
(God said to Abraham)

Rock 'n' Roll

Hold on to the pro-mi-ses of God, hold on to the pro-mi-ses of God, when it's tough and hard in your back yard you got-ta hold on to the pro-mi-ses of God.

1. God said to A-bra-ham, 'Hey, you'll have an heir, get of-fa the floor, stop laugh-ing like a bear'. A-bra-ham said, 'But I'm way past my prime, have you lost count, Lord, 'cause

I'm eigh-ty five'. God said, 'Well, that's no prob-lem to me, be -

lieve what is said 'cause it's meant to be'. You got - ta

2. Now Abraham believed what God said was true,
   but in case he was wrong he had plan number two.
   And through his servant he got himself a son.
   He thought at last the promise had come,
   but God said, 'This is your plan, not mine,
   I'll do it my way and in my time'.

3. God said to Abraham, 'Look up in the sky,
   count all the stars way, way up high.
   That's the size of family I'll give to you,
   if you obey what I say in all you do.
   That's the good news, but now here's a surprise,
   the bad news is, you've gotta be circumcised!'

4. So Isaac was born and Abram was proud,
   but a voice from on high came through clear and loud.
   This boy will be a sacrifice.
   Abram said 'Hey, that's not very nice',
   but by now he knew it really paid to obey;
   he said to Isaac, 'We're going out for the day'.

5. Tied hand and foot, on his back Isaac lay,
   as his Dad raised the knife he knew this was not his day!
   But with seconds to spare God stepped in, in time.
   Isaac said, 'Phew! Well, you cut that a bit fine!'
   God said to Abraham, 'You've passed the last test,
   you really have proved you're the best of the best'.

Words and Music: Doug Horley arr. Donald Thomson

111 Hosanna

1. Ho-san-na, ho-san-na, ho-san-na in the high-est! Ho-san-na, ho-san-na, ho-san-na in the high-est! Lord, we lift up your name, with hearts full of praise; be ex-al-ted, O Lord, my God! Ho-san-na in the high-est!

2. Glo-ry, glo-ry, glo-ry to the King of kings! Glo-ry, glo-ry, glo-ry to the King of kings! Glo-ry to the King of kings!

Words and Music: Carl Tuttle

112 How did Moses cross the Red Sea?

Words: Hugh Mitchell
Music: traditional melodies, adapted by Hugh Mitchell arr. Noel Rawsthorne

113 How good of Father God

How good of Fa-ther God to give us gifts we don't de-serve, so

ma-ny ways to de-mon-strate his power! It's just be-cause he loves us and be-

cause he wants to use us. Bring his king-dom to a world that has gone

sour.
Ho - ly Spi-rit, we are rea - dy now,
Spi - rit of Je - sus, come and touch us now, give

wil - ling now to hear and to o - bey.
po - wer for your work through us to - day

Words and Music: Capt. Alan Price, CA

114 I am a lighthouse

I am a light - house, a shin - ing and bright house,
out in the waves of a stor - my sea. The oil of the Spi - rit
keeps my lamp burn - ing; Je - sus, my Lord, is the light in me.
light in me. And when peo-ple see the good things that I do, they'll give

Words and Music: Graham Kendrick

115 I am a new creation

I am a new cre-a-tion, no more in con-dem-na-tion, here in the grace of God I stand. My heart is o-ver-flow-ing, my love just keeps on grow-ing, here in the grace of God I stand. And I will praise you, Lord,

yes, I will praise you, Lord, and I will sing of all that you have done.

A joy that knows no lim - it, a light - ness in my spi - rit, here in the grace of God I stand.

Words and Music: Dave Bilbrough

116 I am a soldier

2. The pow'r of love and the word of the Lord
   is like a mighty two-edged sword.
   God's armour I'll put on with glee,
   it's his protection over me.

3. I'll fight against the wrong I see,
   including ev'ry wrong in me!
   I won't let Satan get a hold,
   I'll trust in Jesus and be bold!

Words and Music: Capt. Alan Price, CA

117 I am fearfully and wonderfully made

1. I am fear - ful - ly and won - der - f'ly made.
I am fear - ful - ly and won - der - f'ly made.
He who put the stars in place, and knows them all by name, has made me fear - ful - ly and won - der - f'ly made.

2. I am

Words and Music: Jim Bailey

118 I am part of God's plan

Chorus

I am part of God's plan, ev-'ry one of us can be too, be part of his plan!

1. Je-sus said his king-dom be-longs to chil-dren such as you and me!
2. His plan is to win back the world, make it what it ought to be!

I'll live as a child of the King, be what he wants me to be!
I'll fight as a child of the King, by the pow-er of his Spi-rit in me!

last time · Fine · *to verses*

D.C.

Words and Music: Capt. Alan Price, CA arr. B. Chesser

119 I am so glad

I am so glad, I am so ve - ry glad that

Je - sus showed his love for me, makes me the best that I can be!

I am so glad, I am so ve - ry glad that

last time to Coda ⊕

Je - sus is the best friend of all! He's al - ways there what -

Words and Music: Capt. Alan Price, CA

120 I am the apple of God's eye
(Spiritual fruit)

With a latin rhythm

1. I am the AP‑PLE of God's eye, his BA‑NA‑NA o‑ver me is love.

He O‑RAN‑GES his an‑gels to look af‑ter me, as his bless‑ings PLUM‑met from a‑bove.

2. Ne‑ver have to play the GOOSE‑BER‑RY,

Words and Music: Jim Bailey

121 I am the way

(Boys) I am the way (I am the way), (Boys) I am the truth (I am the truth),

(Boys) I am the life (I am the life), (All) I am the way, the truth, the life.

(Boys) I am the way (I am the way), (Boys) I am the truth (I am the truth);

(All) no one comes to the Fa-ther, no one comes to the

Fa-ther but by me.

Words and Music: Chris Jackson

© Copyright 1991 Powerpack/Learning Curve Music, P.O. Box 421, Hailsham,
East Sussex, BN27 4ZA, UK. Used by permission.

122 I believe in Jesus

Words and Music: Marc Nelson

123 I can be what God wants me to be

1. I can be what God wants me to be, let the fruit of the Spi - rit
do what God wants me to do, by the po - wer of the

grow in me. More like Je - sus I would be; Ho - ly
Spi - rit too, there are things he's planned for me to do; Ho - ly

Spi - rit, work in me, Ho - ly Spi - rit, work in me. 2. I can
Spi - rit, work in me, Ho - ly Spi - rit, work in me.

Words and Music: Capt. Alan Price, CA arr. Gillian Venton
© Copyright 1996 Daybreak Music Ltd, Silverdale Road, Eastbourne,
East Sussex, BN20 7AB, UK. Used by permission.

124 I can do all, all, all things

2. Make new friends: all things.
   Give and lend: all things.
   Make amends: all things,
   through Christ who strengthens me.

3. Pray and sing: all things.
   Love our King: all things.
   Ev'rything: all things,
   through Christ who strengthens me.

Words and Music: Jim Bailey

125 I could sing unending songs
(The happy song)

Oh, I could sing un-end-ing songs of how you saved my soul. Well, I could dance a thou-sand miles be-cause of your great love.

My heart is burst-ing, Lord, to tell of all you've done. Of how you changed my life and wiped a-way the past.

Words and Music: Martin Smith

126 I'd reach for the stars
(Reach for the stars)

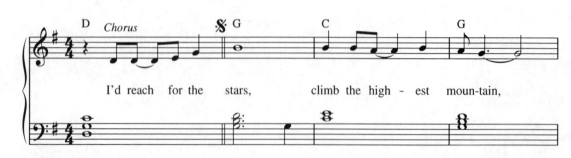

I'd reach for the stars, climb the high-est moun-tain,

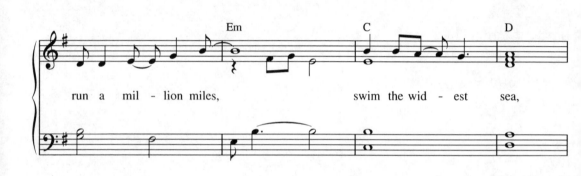

run a mil-lion miles, swim the wid-est sea,

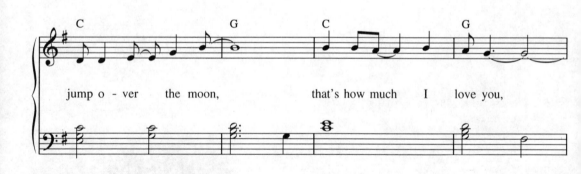

jump o-ver the moon, that's how much I love you,

I'd do a-ny-thing for you, my Lord.

2. What do you ask, what should I do?
   Please help me, Jesus, to follow you.
   I give you my life, I give you my will,
   O Jesus, I want you to know . . .

Words and Music: Mike Burn

127 If I look in a mirror

If I look in a mir-ror and there I see my

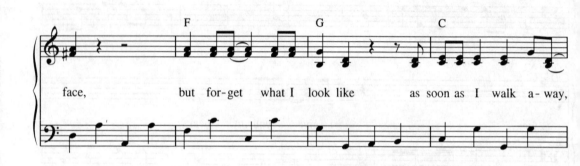

face, but for-get what I look like as soon as I walk a-way,

that is what it's like if I hear God's

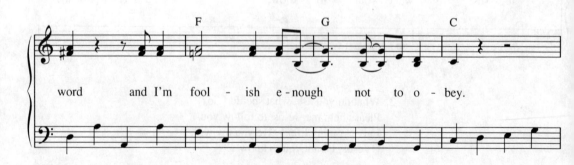

word and I'm fool-ish e-nough not to o-bey.

'Cos hap - py are those who hear the word of God,

hap - py are those who trust it and o - bey.

No o - ther way to find true hap - pi - ness than to

hear the word of God and o - bey.

Words and Music: Mike Burn arr. Donald Thomson

128 If I were a butterfly
(The butterfly song)

Brightly, with swing

1. If I were a but-ter-fly, I'd thank you, Lord, for giv-ing me wings, and if I were a ro-bin in a tree, I'd thank you, Lord, that I could sing, and if I were a fish in the sea, I'd wig-gle my tail and I'd gig-gle with glee; but I just thank you, Fa-ther, for mak-ing me 'me.'

Chorus

For you gave me a heart, and you gave me a smile, you gave me Je-sus and you made me your child, and I just thank you, Fa-ther, for mak-ing me 'me'.

2. If I were an elephant,
   I'd thank you, Lord, by raising my trunk,
   and if I were a kangaroo,
   you know I'd hop right up to you,
   and if I were an octopus,
   I'd thank you, Lord, for my fine looks;
   but I just thank you, Father, for making me 'me'.

3. If I were a wiggly worm,
   I'd thank you, Lord, that I could squirm,
   and if I were a billy goat,
   I'd thank you, Lord, for my strong throat,
   and if I were a fuzzy wuzzy bear,
   I'd thank you, Lord, for my fuzzy wuzzy hair;
   but I just thank you, Father, for making me 'me'.

Words: Brian Howard
Music: Brian Howard arr. Noel Rawsthorne

129 If Jesus is de vine

In a calypso style

1. If Je-sus is de vine,

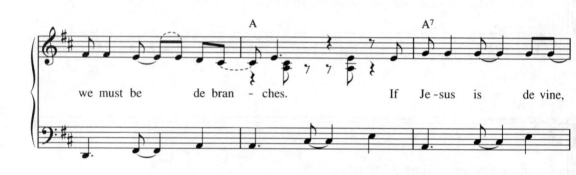

we must be de bran - ches. If Je-sus is de vine,

we must be de bran - ches. If

Je-sus is de vine, we must be de bran-

- ches,   and   bear fruit in   the   king - dom   of   God.

2. If

2. If Jesus is de rock, we should be a little bolder.
     If Jesus is de rock, we should be a little bolder.
     If Jesus is de rock, we should be a little bolder,
     to bear fruit in the kingdom of God.

3. If Jesus is de bread, is your name on the roll now?
     If Jesus is de bread, is your name on the roll now?
     If Jesus is de bread, is your name on the roll now,
     to bear fruit in the kingdom of God?

Words and Music: Sammy Horner

130 If we admit to God

Words and Music: Kath Fathers

131 If you feel unhappy
(Jesus loves even you)

2. If you want to cry when you watch your TV,
   don't hold it back, don't hold it back,
   for Jesus cries too for those children you see,
   Jesus loves even you.

3. Tonight when you go to your bedroom to sleep,
   don't be afraid, don't be afraid,
   for Jesus has promised our souls he will keep,
   Jesus loves even you.

Words and Music: Sammy Horner

132 If you're going to run the race and win
(Run the race)

If you're going to run the race and win, you've got to know where to begin. You need to learn about the Lord, and start by reading his Word.

1. Reading his Word, Genesis and Exodus. Reading his Word, Leviticus and Numbers. Reading his Word, Deuteronomy, Joshua and

Jud - ges. Read-ing his Word, Ruth, Sa-muel and Kings. If you're

CODA

Word. And start by read-ing his Word. And Word.

2. Reading his Word, Chronicles and Ezra.
   Reading his Word, Nehemiah and Esther.
   Reading his Word, Job, Psalms and Proverbs.
   Reading his Word, Ecclesiastes and Song of Solomon.

3. Reading his Word, Isaiah and Jeremiah.
   Reading his Word, Lamentations and Ezekiel.
   Reading his Word, Daniel and Hosea.
   Reading his Word, Joel and Amos.

4. Reading his Word, Obadiah and Jonah.
   Reading his Word, Micah and Nahum.
   Reading his Word, Habakkuk and Zephaniah.
   Reading his Word, Haggai, Zechariah and Malachi.

5. Reading his Word, Matthew, Mark, Luke and John.
   Reading his Word, Acts, Romans and Corinthians.
   Reading his Word, Galatians, Ephesians and Philippians.
   Reading his Word, Colossians, Thessalonians and Timothy.

6. Reading his Word, Titus and Philemon.
   Reading his Word, Hebrews and James.
   Reading his Word, the letters of Peter and John.
   Reading his Word, Jude and Revelation.

Words and Music: Ian White arr. Donald Thomson

133 If your output exceeds your input
(Input/output)

Rock 'n' roll
Capo 3

If your out-put ex-ceeds your in-put,

your up-keep will be your

down-fall. But if your in-put

ex-ceeds your out-put, you can hold your

head up and push the e-ne-my down.

Words and Music: Richard Hubbard arr. Donald Thomson

134 If you see a special way
(God uses kids!)

1. If you see a spe-cial way to give the Lord's great love a-way, you don't have to wait till you're grown up, 'cos God can use you now. If you want to tell some-one the spe-cial things that the Lord has done, you don't have to wait, 'cos God can use you now!

2. I can pray for God to bring
   people that I love to him,
   I don't have to wait till I'm grown up
   'cos God can use me now.
   I can pray with others who
   want to know God's healing too,
   I don't have to wait,
   'cos God can use me now!

Words and Music: Peter and Hanneke Jacobs

135 I have hidden your word

I have hid-den your word in my heart, that I might not sin a-gainst you. I have hid-den your word in my heart, that I might not sin a-gainst you, that I might not sin a-gainst you, that I might not sin a-gainst you. I have hid-den your word in my heart, that I might not sin a-gainst you.

Words and Music: Mick Gisbey

136 I just want to thank you, Lord
(My guiding light)

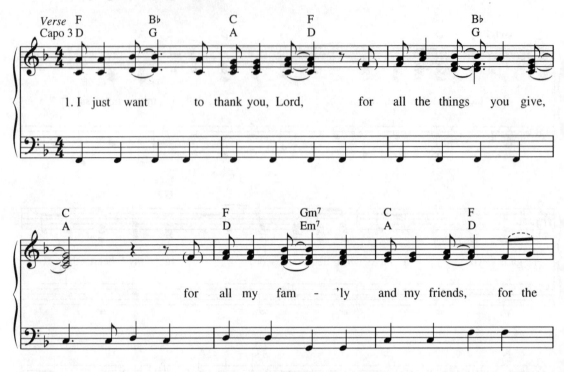

1. I just want to thank you, Lord, for all the things you give, for all my fam - 'ly and my friends, for the

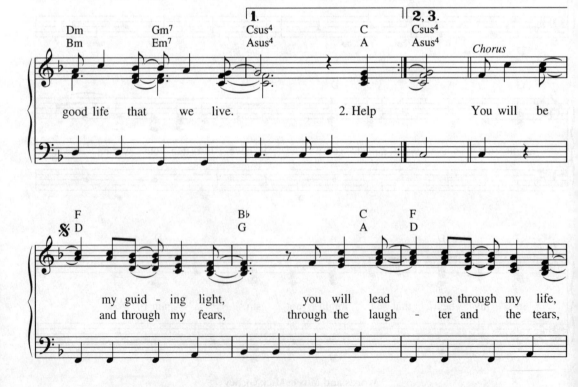

good life that we live. 2. Help   You will be

my guid - ing light,   you will lead   me through my life,
and through my fears,   through the laugh - ter and the tears,

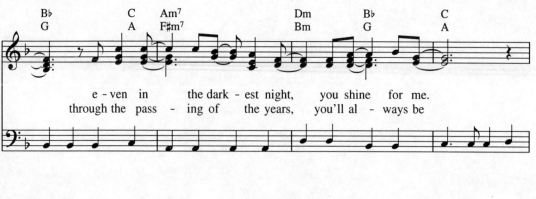

e - ven in the dark - est night, you shine for me.
through the pass - ing of the years, you'll al - ways be

Through my doubts my guid - ing light.

2. Help me learn to look to you,
   and care for others more.
   Help me trust in you each day,
   whenever I'm unsure.

3. Lead me always in your steps,
   beautiful and true.
   Jesus, you will light the way,
   and I will follow you.

Words and Music: Paul Field

137 I love the lights on the Christmas trees

I love the lights on the Christ-mas trees, I love the ca-rols we sing, I love the ma-gic of Christ-mas time, but most of all I love Je-sus, my King. We ce-le-brate the birth-day of Je-sus, God's Son, who left the glo-ry of hea-ven and was born a ba-by in Beth-le-hem, (a ti-ny ba-by like ev-'ry-one). (a hu-man ba-by like ev-'ry-one). I most of all I love Je-sus, my King!

Words and Music: Capt. Alan Price, CA arr. Gillian Venton
© Copyright 1996 Daybreak Music Ltd, Silverdale Road, Eastbourne,
East Sussex, BN20 7AB, UK. Used by permission.

138 I love to be with you, Jesus
(To be with you)

I love to be with you, Je-sus, lis-t'ning to your voice, and when I hear you speak my name, my heart and soul re-joice. And if you said 'jump', I'd jump for joy, and if you said 'run', I'd run to your side, and if you said 'leap', I'd take a

Words and Music: Mike Burn arr. Donald Thomson

139 I love you, Lord Jesus

I love you, Lord Je-sus, the King of all things. You

love me, Lord Je - sus, your love ne -ver ends. To

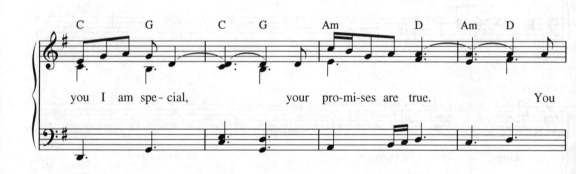

you I am spe - cial, your pro-mi-ses are true. You

love me, Lord Je - sus, and Lord, I love you.

140 I'm accepted, I'm forgiven

Words and Music: Rob Hayward

141 I'm a full-time Christian

Verse

1. I'm a full-time Christian, working for the Lord, I'm trying to honour Jesus, not seeking a reward. Whatever I do, I do for him, and try my best, you see, so glory goes to Father God, and not just to me.

2. I'm a full-time Christian, whatever I may be, playing, working, or at home, watching the T-V. I'll make mistakes, I'll get things wrong, but I will try and see, that glory goes to Father God and isn't spoilt by me.

I'll work for Je-

sus, what-e - ver I do, I'll work for Je -

- sus, why don't you? I'll work for Je - sus,

come what may, I'll work for Je - sus ev - 'ry day!

Words and Music: Capt. Alan Price, CA

142 I'm a pow pow powerpack!

I'm a pow pow pow pow pow pow pow pow-er-pack!

I'm a pow pow pow pow pow pow pow pow-er-pack!

1. I may be small but I'm pow-er-ful, God has made me that way, re-
2. Be-ing con-nec-ted to Je-sus lights me on my way,

charged by the Ho-ly Spi - rit ev-'ry day. I'm a
giv-ing me the pow - er to live each day.

pow pow pow pow pow pow pow, pow pow pow pow pow pow pow-er-pack!

Words and Music: Ron Sivers

© Copyright 1989 Wellingborough Christian Centre, St John Street, Wellingborough,
Northamptonshire, NN8 4LG, UK. Used by permission.

143 I'm a winner

Words and Music: Ron Sivers

© Copyright 1988 Wellingborough Christian Centre, St John Street, Wellingborough, Northamptonshire, NN8 4LG, UK. Used by permission.

144 I may live in a great big city

I may live in a great big ci-ty, I may live in a

vil-lage small, I may live in a ti-ny house, I

may live in a tow-er tall, I may live in the

coun-try-side, I may live by the sea,

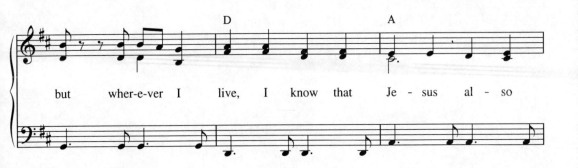

but   wher-e-ver I   live,   I   know that   Je - sus   al - so

lives   with   me,   but   wher-e - ver I   live,   I   know

Je - sus lives with   me.   me,   but   wher-e - ver I

live,   I   know   Je - sus   lives   with   me.

Words and Music: Ian Smale arr. Donald Thomson

145 I'm enthusiastic

2. I'm gonna work and do what I can do.
   Read my Bible, pray and worship too,
   yes I will, yes I will, yes I will!

Words and Music: Capt. Alan Price, CA arr. Gillian Venton
© Copyright 1996 Daybreak Music Ltd, Silverdale Road, Eastbourne,
East Sussex, BN20 7AB, UK. Used by permission.

146 I'm getting to know God as my Dad

I'm get-ting to know God as my Dad,

I'm get-ting to know God as my Fa - ther;

it's me-ga, yeah! to know he loves and cares,

yes, I'm get-ting to know I've a Dad up -stairs.

Words and Music: Jim Bailey

147 I'm gonna be a mighty warrior
(Mighty warrior)

Words and Music: Christopher Jackson

148 I'm gonna build my house on solid rock

With a bouncy feel

Chorus

I'm gon-na build my house on so - lid rock, I'm gon-na

build my house on so - lid rock, so I don't wake up to a

nas - ty shock, to find no-thing but a pile of rub-ble.

last time

to verses

rub-ble. *Verse* 1. Don't want to build a house on foun -

da - tions that will wob-ble. Don't want to build a house with

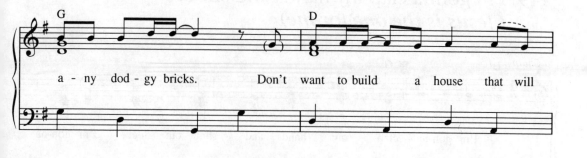

a - ny dod - gy bricks.   Don't want to build   a house   that will

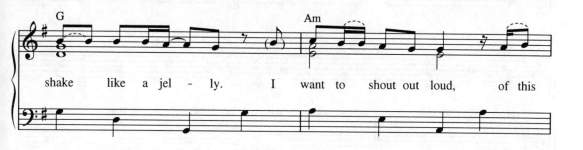

shake   like   a jel - ly.   I   want to   shout out loud,   of this

house   you   can   be   proud!   I'm gon - na

2. Jesus said, 'Take my words and put them into action;
   make these words', he said, 'foundations in your life.
   Build with care or else your house will surely tumble,
   and it's not a clever trick to own a heap of bricks.'

3. Jesus said, 'Take my words and put them into action;
   make these words', he said, 'foundations in your life.
   And when the river comes and crashes up against you,
   you won't get washed away, instead you'll cheer and say:

   Yes, I built my house on solid rock,
   yes, I built my house on solid rock,
   and I won't wake up to a nasty shock,
   to find nothing but a pile of rubble.'

Words and Music: Doug Horley

149 I'm gonna clap my hands and shout
(*Jesus is the one for me*)

I'm gon-na clap my hands and shout out loud, I'm gon-na raise my voice a-bove the crowd, be-cause Je - sus is the one for me. I'm gon-na dance and cheer and stamp my feet, I'm gon-na sing this song walk-ing down the street, be-cause Je - sus is the one for me.

Words and Music: John Fryer

150 I'm gonna click

Capo 3

1. I'm gon-na click, click, click, I'm gon-na clap, clap, clap, I'm gon-na click, I'm gon-na clap and praise the Lord! Be-cause of all he's done I'm gon-na make him 'num-ber one', I'm gon-na click, I'm gon-na clap and praise the Lord! I'm gon-na Lord!

to repeat *last time* *D.S.*

2. I'm gonna zoom, zoom, zoom,
   around the room, room, room,
   I'm gonna zoom around the room and praise the Lord!
   Because of all he's done, I'm gonna make him 'number one',
   I'm gonna zoom around the room and praise the Lord!

3. I'm gonna sing, sing, sing,
   I'm gonna shout, shout, shout,
   I'm gonna sing, I'm gonna shout and praise the Lord!
   Because of all he's done, I'm gonna make him 'number one',
   I'm gonna sing, I'm gonna shout and praise the Lord!

4. I'm gonna click, click, click,
   I'm gonna clap, clap, clap,
   I'm gonna zoom around the room and praise the Lord!
   Because of all he's done, I'm gonna make him 'number one',
   I'm gonna sing, I'm gonna shout and praise the Lord!

Words and Music: adapted Capt. Alan Price, CA arr. B. Chesser
© Copyright 1991 Daybreak Music Ltd, Silverdale Road, Eastbourne,
East Sussex, BN20 7AB, UK. Used by permission.

151 I'm gonna dance on the streets
(Dance on the streets)

I'm gon-na dance on the streets, I'm gon-na sing in the rain,

for the Spi - rit of God

is poured out a -gain. I'm gon-na shout it a - loud,

I'm gon - na let the world know

that the ri - ver of God has start - ed to flow.

Words and Music: Mike Burn arr. Donald Thomson

152 I'm gonna shine
(Shine, shine, shine)

Allegro

Chorus

I'm gon-na shine, shine, shine, a light in the world I'll be.

I want to shine, shine, shine, let

peo-ple see Je - sus in me! me! 1. I want to glo - ri -

fy the Fa - ther by the things I do; be the per - son

God has made me, let - ting his love flow through! I'm gon-na

2. And when it's hard 'n' it's not so easy
to know and do what's right;
I'll trust the Holy Spirit in me,
to help me win each fight.

3. Even if I fail him often
and my light is dim;
he has promised to forgive me,
I can come back to him!

Words and Music: Capt. Alan Price, CA

© Copyright 1990 Daybreak Music Ltd, Silverdale Road, Eastbourne,
East Sussex, BN20 7AB, UK. Used by permission.

153 I'm gonna walk by faith

I'm gon - na walk by faith, not by sight; I'm gon - na

walk by faith, not by sight. I'm gon-na fol-low Je - sus, and

do what's right; I'm gon-na walk by faith, not by sight. Je -sus

said, 'If you fol - low me, you will ne -ver live in dark - ness'.

Words and Music: Jim Bailey arr. Donald Thomson

154 I'm in-right, out-right, up-right, down-right happy

Words: Capt. Alan Price, CA
Music: unknown arr. Gillian Venton
Words © Copyright 1996 Daybreak Music Ltd, Silverdale Road, Eastbourne,
East Sussex, BN20 7AB, UK. Used by permission.

155 I'm just a shepherd
(David and Goliath)

1. I'm just a shep-herd, Da - vid is my name, I live in a vil-lage called Beth - le - hem. My bro-thers are sol - diers and they're fight-ing in the war, but I don't un-der-stand what the fight-ing is for! I don't un-der-stand what the fight-ing is for! 2. I go to see my bro-thers and I bring them cheese and bread, I see Go-li - ath and I hear the things he says, he's big and mean and ug - ly, he's a

I've got the fire of the Lord in-side! I've got the fire of the

last time   *to continue*   *Verse*

Lord in-side!   Lord in-side! 4. Well, Go-liath,   you can fight   me with your

spear and with your sword, but   I come a-gainst you in the name of the Lord! And

ev-'ry-one who ga-thers here will un-der-stand   the bat-tle is the Lord's and it's

in our hands,   the bat-tle is the Lord's and it's   in our hands! Well,

Words and Music: Ian White

156 I'm putting God's armour on

I'm put-ting God's ar-mour on,　I'm put-ting God's ar-mour on,

so I can stand　in his might,　fight for what is right　and

walk　in the light　of the Lord.　I'm put-ting God's Lord.　Lord

I put　on　the breast-plate of right-eous-ness,　put

truth a-round my waist　like a belt,　I put　on　the

Words and Music: Mike Burn arr. Donald Thomson

157 I'm putting God's gear on
(What a team we make)

I'm put-ting God's gear on and I am feel-ing strong, be-cause I know the Lord is

ne - ver wrong. For he has made it clear that he is al - ways near, and his

per - fect love gets rid of fear. So as I run the race at

Je-sus' pace, at the fin-ish-ing line there'll be no dis-grace. Lord,

I love you, and you love me too, what a team we make.

Words and Music: Ian Smale arr. Donald Thomson

158 I'm putting my hand in your hand

Words and Music: Steve Bradshaw

159 I'm singing your praise, Lord

2. I'm clapping my hands . . .

3. I'm shouting your name . . .

4. I'm jumping for joy . . .

Words and Music: Mike Burn

160 I'm so excited

Verse

1. I'm so ex-ci-ted, Lord, I can't keep still; I've got to jump up and down on my feet,

'cos when I think a-bout the way that you love me, Lord, I

know I can't just sit in my seat, no. Ooh, it starts in my heart

now, then it flows through my bo - dy.

Ooh, this feel-ing in-side me, I know that it's you. I just can't

2. Just being here with you is oh so precious,
   it's a feeling I will never forget,
   and now I feel your Spirit moving within me,
   Lord, I thank you for this moment we share, yeah.

Words and Music: Audrey Traynor

161 I'm sorry

1. I'm sor - ry for the wrong I've done, I'm
sor - ry for the wrong I've done; please for-give me, Lord,
please for-give me, Lord, I'm sor - ry for the wrong I've done. me!

2. I'm sorry for the wrong I've said,
   I'm sorry for the wrong I've said;
   please forgive me, Lord,
   please forgive me, Lord,
   I'm sorry for the wrong I've said.

3. I'm sorry for the wrong I've thought,
   I'm sorry for the wrong I've thought;
   please forgive me, Lord,
   please forgive me, Lord,
   I'm sorry for the wrong I've thought.

4. Thank you for forgiving me,
   thank you for forgiving me;
   thank you, thank you, Lord,
   thank you, thank you, Lord,
   thank you for forgiving me.

Words and Music: Capt. Alan Price, CA arr. Donald Thomson
© Copyright 1998 Daybreak Music Ltd, Silverdale Road, Eastbourne,
East Sussex, BN20 7AB, UK. Used by permission.

162 I'm special

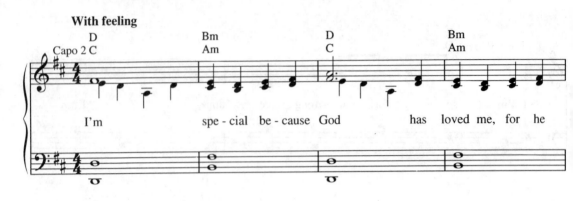

I'm spe-cial be-cause God has loved me, for he

gave the best thing that he had to save me;

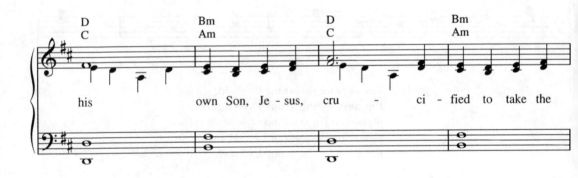

his own Son, Je-sus, cru - ci - fied to take the

blame, for all the bad things I have done.

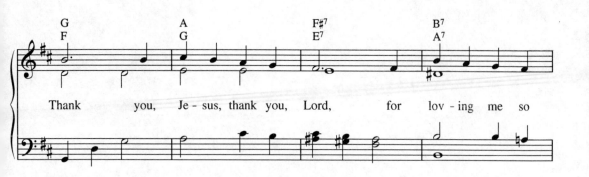

Thank you, Je-sus, thank you, Lord, for lov-ing me so

much. I know I don't de - serve a - ny - thing;

help me feel your love right now to know deep in my

heart that I'm your spe - cial friend.

Words and Music: Graham Kendrick

163 I'm taking on board

1. Leader sings

2. All sing
   As verse one but replace 'I'm' with 'We're'

Words and Music: Ian Smale

164 I'm working out what it means to follow Jesus
(The calculator song)

I'm work - ing out what it means to fol -low Je - sus,

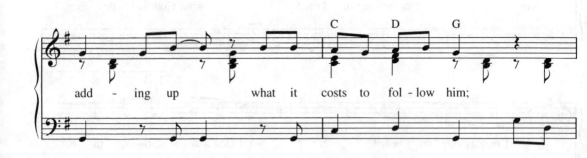

add - ing up what it costs to fol - low him;

count -ing the times that his love is mul - ti - ply - ing,

re - a - lis - ing he took a - way my sin. He's

al - ways in my me - mo - ry, he'll ne - ver can - cel what he's done for me. When I add it to - ge - ther I cal - cu - late Je - sus is great, Je - sus is great!

1.

2.

Words and Music: Jim Bailey

165 I'm your child

1. I'm your child and you are my God. I thank you, Father, for your loving care. I'm your child and you are my God. You've made me special and you're always there.

2. I'm your child and you are my God.
I love you, Jesus, you're close to me.
I'm your child and you are my God.
I give you worship, I bow the knee.

3. I'm your child and you are my God.
Holy Spirit, flow out to me.
I'm your child and you are my God.
You give me power and authority.

Words and Music: Richard Hubbard

166 In all the galaxy there is no one else like me
(No one else like me)

In all the ga-lax-y there is no one else like me, I'm a u-nique part of Fa-ther God's cre-a-tion. Some-times weak and some-times strong, do-ing right or do-ing wrong, God loves this u-nique part of his cre-a-tion.

No mat-ter how I feel a-bout my-self, I'm the ob-ject of God's care; he sent his son that I might know his love, all the time and ev-'ry-where! In

Words and Music: Capt. Alan Price, CA

167 In days of old

In days of old when knights were bold and kings ruled the land,
ev-'ry-one knew just what to do when they gave a com-mand.
Some kings ruled with kind-ness, and o-thers were so mean, but
we have a King named Je - sus, the best there's e - ver been!

Words and Music: Capt. Alan Price, CA

168 I need faith

2. I need faith if I'm gonna hear the words you say to me,
   I need faith if I'm gonna be what you want me to be.
   I need faith, faith, faith, faith,
   faith ev'ry second of my life.

3. I need faith 'cause I really want to see your kingdom come,
   I need faith just to know where all my strength is coming from.
   I need faith, faith, faith, faith,
   faith ev'ry second of my life.

Words and Music: Sammy Horner arr. Gillian Venton
© Copyright 1996 Daybreak Music Ltd, Silverdale Road, Eastbourne,
East Sussex, BN20 7AB, UK. Used by permission.

169 In everything that I do
(Show me)

Words and Music: Ian White

170 I once was frightened

1.I once was frightened of spi - ders, I once was fright-ened of the dark; I once was fright - ened by ma - ny, ma - ny things, es - pe - cial-ly things that barked. But now I'm ask - ing Je - sus to help these fears to go, 'cause I don't want them to be part of me, no, no, no, no, no.

2. I once was frightened by thunder,
and frightened of lightning too;
I once was frightened by many, many things
that crashed and banged and blew.
But now I'm asking Jesus . . .

Words and Music: Ian Smale

171 I reach up high

2. May my whole life be a song of praise,
   to worship God in ev'ry way.
   In this song the actions praise his name,
   I want my actions ev'ry day to do the same.

Words and Music: Judy Bailey arr. Donald Thomson

172 Is it spooky

2. But through the Holy Spirit,
   supernaturally,
   he gives us words and pictures,
   a gift of prophecy. Oh, . . .

3. So we should learn to listen
   to all that God would say,
   and act on what we think he's said,
   listen and obey. Oh, . . .

Words and Music: Capt. Alan Price, CA arr. Gillian Venton
© Copyright 1996 Daybreak Music Ltd, Silverdale Road, Eastbourne,
East Sussex, BN20 7AB, UK. Used by permission.

173 Isn't it good

Is-n't it good to be to-ge-ther, be-ing with friends old and new? Is-n't it good? The Bi-ble tells us Je-sus, our Lord, is here too! too! He's here! By his Spi-rit he's with us, he's here! His pro-mise is true, he's here! Though we can't see him, he's here for me and for you! He's here for me and for you!

174 It's an adventure

Words and Music: Capt. Alan Price, CA

175 It's great

Allegro

It's great, great, great, com-ing a-long; it's great, great, great to be-long; it's great to know we're not wrong; it's great that Je-sus loves us! It's great, great, great to be here; it's great, great, know-ing he's near; it's great ev-'ry-bo-dy can hear; it's great that Je-sus loves us! It's great that Je-sus loves us!

Words and Music: Capt. Alan Price, CA

© Copyright 1990 Daybreak Music Ltd, Silverdale Road, Eastbourne,
East Sussex, BN20 7AB, UK. Used by permission.

176 It takes an almighty hand

It takes an al-migh-ty hand, to make your har-vest grow; it takes an al-migh-ty hand, how-e-ver you may sow. It takes an al-migh-ty hand, the world a-round me shows; it takes the al-migh-ty hand of God.

1. It takes his hand to grow your gar-den,

all from a se - cret in a seed; part of a
plan he spoke and star - ted, and said is
've - ry good in - deed'. It takes an al -

2. It takes his hand to turn the seasons,
   to give the sun and snow their hour;
   and in this plan we learn his reason,
   his nature and eternal power.

3. It took his hand to carry sorrow,
   for ev'ry sin that we have done;
   and on a cross he bought tomorrow,
   a world of good, like he'd begun.

4. And in his hands there is perfection,
   that in this land we only taste;
   for now, we see a poor reflection,
   then, we shall see him face to face.

Words and Music: Ian White arr. Donald Thomson

177 I walk by faith

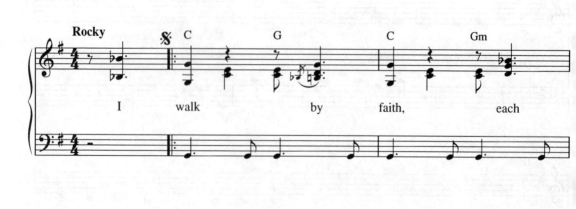

I walk by faith, each

step by faith, to live by

faith, I put my trust in you.   I

Ev - 'ry step I take

Words and Music: Chris Falson

178 I wanna be a light

2. You take away all my fear,
   you fill me with your love.
   You give me strength so I can sing
   songs of praise to my King.

Words and Music: Nigel Hemming arr. Donald Thomson

179 I wanna tell you
(Heavenly Father)

1. I wan-na tell you how much I love you
   how much we love

you. I wan-na tell you how much I care.
you. We wan-na tell you how much we care.

Hea-ven-ly Fa - ther, we are your child-

-ren, when we need you, you'll be there.

1.
2. We wan - na tell

2. *D.S.*

Words and Music: Sammy Horner

180 I want to be a tree that's bearing fruit
(I want to be a blooming tree)

I want to be a tree that's bear-ing fruit, that God has pruned and caused to shoot, Oh, up in the sky, so ve-ry, ve-ry high. I want to be, I want to be a bloom-ing tree. God has pro-mised his Ho-ly Spi-rit will wa-ter our roots and help us grow. Lis-ten and o-bey, and be-fore you know it your fruit will start to grow, grow, grow, grow, grow.

Words and Music: Doug Horley

181 I want to be like Jesus

Gently

Verse D ... Em⁷ ... D ... G ... A

1. I want to be like Je - sus, I want to love like Je - sus,
   I want to care like he does, I want to share like he does,

I want to lis - ten to his word.
I want to be a child of

G ... A ... *Chorus* G ... Bm

God. Make me more, make me

Em⁷ ... G ... Bm ... Em⁷

more like Je - sus. More, make me more like Je -

to continue ... *last time*
D.C.

D

sus.

2. I want to be like Jesus,
   I want to see like Jesus,
   I want to feel the Father's heart.
   I want to reach like he does
   with love to each like he does,
   I want to be a child of God.

Words and Music: Claire Morgans

182 I want to be salt for Jesus
(Salt for Jesus)

I want to be salt for Je - sus, salt in the world for him, spread-ing the fla-vour of Je - sus, stir-ring his good - ness in. I've got the taste of Je - sus, I know what he can do! I want to be salt for Je - sus, so you can know him too.

Words and Music: Capt. Alan Price, CA arr. D. Coad

183 I want to worship you

I want to wor - ship you all of my life, give you praise. I want to serve on - ly you all of my life, all my days. For you are a migh - ty awe - some God, and you reign in pow'r and you reign in love. O Lord, you are God.

Words and Music: Chris Jackson

184 I will dance, I will sing
(Undignified)

With life and energy

I will dance, I will sing, to be mad for my King.

No-thing, Lord, is hin-der-ing the pas-sion in my soul.

pas-sion in my soul. And I'll be-come

e-ven more un-dig-ni-fied than this.

Words and Music: Matt Redman

185 I will enter his gates
(He has made me glad)

With pace and swing

I will en-ter his gates with thanks-giv-ing in my heart, I will en-ter his courts with praise, I will say this is the day that the Lord has made, I will re-joice for he has made me glad. He has made me glad, he has made me glad, I

will re - joice for he has made me glad.

He has made me glad, he has made me glad, I

will re - joice for he has made me glad.

Words and Music: Leona von Brethorst

186 I will offer up my life
(This thankful heart)

1. I will of-fer up my life in spi-rit and truth, pour-ing out the oil of love as my wor-ship to you. In sur-ren-der I must give my ev-'ry part; Lord, re-ceive the sac-ri-fice of a bro-ken heart.

Je-sus, what can I give, what can I bring to so faith-ful a friend,

2. You deserve my ev'ry breath
   for you've paid the great cost;
   giving up your life to death,
   even death on a cross.
   You took all my shame away,
   there defeated my sin,
   opened up the gates of heav'n,
   and have beckoned me in.

Words and Music: Matt Redman

187 I will show you my faith

I will show you my faith by my ac-tions, I will show you my faith
by the things I do. I will show you my faith by my ac-tions.
I will glo-ri-fy you. I want my life
to make a diff-'rence,

I want to tell of your great love,

to share my faith with oth – ers, to

do what you would do. Oh, I want to be a help

to you, Lord.

Words and Music: Chris Jackson

188 I will wave my hands

Words and Music: Ian Smale

189 I won't wander off

I won't wan-der off in the dark - ness, I

don't want to live in the cold. I'm not going to live like a

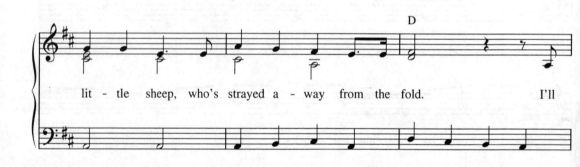

lit - tle sheep, who's strayed a - way from the fold. I'll

try and o-bey the good Shep - herd, as I'm one of his fa - mi - ly,

I'm stay - ing close to Je - sus 'cos that's the

ve - ry best place for me to be, that's the ve - ry best place to

be. be. That's the ve - ry best place for

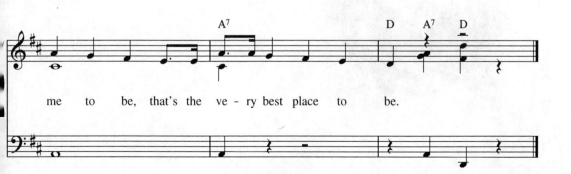

me to be, that's the ve - ry best place to be.

Words and Music: Ian Smale

190 Jehovah Jireh, God will provide

Accelerating

1. Je-ho-vah Ji - reh, God will pro-vide, Je-ho-vah Ro - phe, God heals; Je-ho-vah M'-ked - desh, God who sanc-ti-fies, Je-ho-vah Nis-si, God is my ban-ner.

2. Je-ho-vah Ro - hi, God my shep-herd, Je-ho-vah Sha - lom, God is peace; Je-ho-vah Tsid-ke - nu, God our right-eous-ness, Je-ho-vah Sham-mah, God who is there.

Words and Music: Ian Smale arr. Donald Thomson

© Copyright 1987 Kingsway's Thankyou Music, P.O. Box 75, Eastbourne, East Sussex, BN23 6NW, UK. Used by permission.

191 Jesus came proclaiming
(A deputy for Jesus)

1. Jesus came proclaiming God's kingdom was at hand, for all who would believe in him, obeying his command; and now he sends his deputies like you and me today, to share God's love in ev'ry-thing we do and what we say. I've got my badge inside, I'm a deputy for Jesus, by the Holy Spirit I am

marked and kept for God. I'll wear my badge with pride, I'm a de - pu - ty for Je - sus, un - der his au - tho - ri - ty to live and work for God!

2. Set live and work for God!

2. Set captives free from Satan's grip,
pray for the sick as well,
wherever you may find yourself,
the Good News you must tell!
As Jesus sent disciples then,
he sends us out today,
as deputies for Jesus
we'll follow and obey.

Words and Music: Capt. Alan Price, CA arr. D. Coad

192 Jesus Christ
(Once again)

Thoughtfully, not too fast

Verse

1. Je - sus Christ, I think up - on your sac - ri - fice;
you be - came no - thing, poured out to death.

Ma - ny times I've won - dered at your gift of life, and
I'm in that place once a - gain, I'm in that place once a - gain.

Chorus

And once a - gain I look up - on the

2. Now you are exalted to the highest place,
King of the heavens, where one day I'll bow.
But for now I marvel at this saving grace,
and I'm full of praise once again,
I'm full of praise once again.

Words and Music: Matt Redman arr. Donald Thomson

193 Jesus Christ is the Lord of all

Words and Music: Steve Israel and Gerrit Gustafson

194 Jesus' hands were kind hands

Je - sus' hands were kind hands do - ing good to all,

heal - ing pain and sick - ness, bless - ing child - ren small;

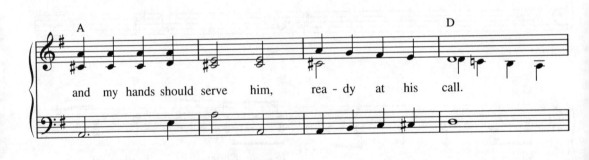

and my hands should serve him, rea - dy at his call.

Je - sus' hands were kind hands do - ing good to all.

Words: Margaret Cropper adapt. Stephen Hopkinson
Music: traditional French melody arr. Donald Thomson

195 Jesus is a friend of mine

With child-like simplicity

1. Je-sus is a friend of mine, praise him.
Je-sus is a friend of mine, praise him.
Praise him, praise him.
Je-sus is a friend of mine, praise him.

2. Jesus died to set us free, praise him . . .

3. He gave us the victory, praise him . . .

4. Jesus is the King of kings, praise him . . .

Words and Music: Paul Mazak arr. Donald Thomson

196 Jesus is greater

Je - sus is great-er than the great-est he - roes, Je - sus is clo-ser than the

clo-sest friends. He came from hea-ven and he died to save us, to

show us love that ne - ver ends. Son of God,

and the Lord of glo - ry, he's the light, fol-low in

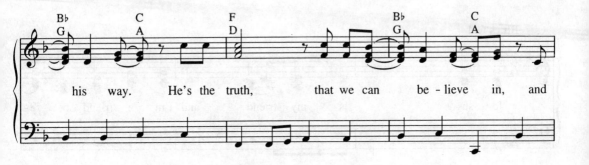

his   way.   He's the truth,   that we can   be - lieve   in,   and

he's the life, he's liv - ing to - day.   Son of God,

Words and Music: Gill Hutchinson

197 Jesus is my friend

Words and Music: Julia Plaut

198 Jesus isn't dead any more

2. He went back to be with God,
   but we know he's still near;
   Jesus sent the Spirit of God,
   and he is always here with us.

Words and Music: Capt. Alan Price, CA

199 Jesus is our shepherd
(The sheep song)

Je - sus is our shep-herd, we must be his

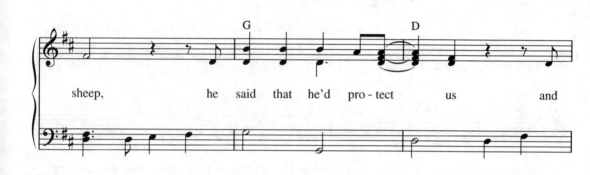

sheep, he said that he'd pro - tect us and

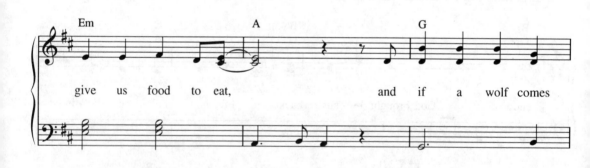

give us food to eat, and if a wolf comes

close to us a shep - herd makes him flee,

I don't mind be-ing in his flock, it does-n't sound baa'd to

me. It does-n't sound baa'd to me, it

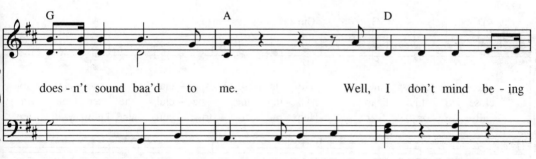

does-n't sound baa'd to me. Well, I don't mind be-ing

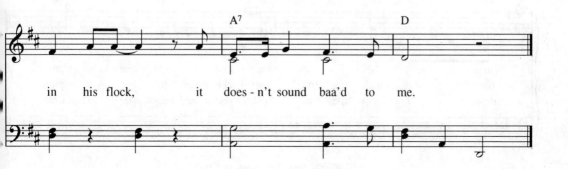

in his flock, it does-n't sound baa'd to me.

Words and Music: Sammy Horner

200 Jesus is special

Gently

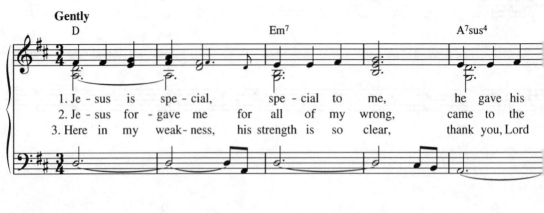

1. Je - sus is spe - cial, spe - cial to me, he gave his
2. Je - sus for - gave me for all of my wrong, came to the
3. Here in my weak - ness, his strength is so clear, thank you, Lord

life so I could be free. He is my friend who
earth so we could be - long in his king - dom,
Je - sus, you're migh - ty, yet here. I praise you for ta - king

ne - ver leaves me. He is so spe - cial, spe - cial to
close to his heart. Mak - ing me spe - cial, he set me a -
all of my fear. Help me to trust you and know you are

me; he is so spe - cial, spe - cial to me.
part; mak - ing me spe - cial, he set me a - part.
near; help me to trust you and know you are near.

Words and Music: Sarah Clark

201 Jesus is the lighthouse

1. Je - sus is the light-house, shin - ing all a - round, shin-ing in the dark-ness, where ev - il things a-bound. Je-sus is the light-house, show-ing us the way, we can leave the dark-ness, live the Je - sus way.

2. Jesus is the foghorn when trouble's very near,
   when hidden dangers threaten, his warning sound you hear.
   Jesus is the lighthouse, showing us the way,
   we can miss the dangers, live the Jesus way.

3. Shine your light in me, Lord, I want to live for you,
   help me shine for you, Lord, in all I say and do.
   I want to be a lighthouse for Jesus ev'ry day,
   help me make a diff'rence in your world, I pray!

Words and Music: Capt. Alan Price, CA arr. B. Chesser
© Copyright 1991 Daybreak Music Ltd, Silverdale Road, Eastbourne,
East Sussex, BN20 7AB, UK. Used by permission.

202 Jesus is the password
(Password)

Je - sus is the pass - word, pass it on.

Je - sus is the pass - word, pass it on.

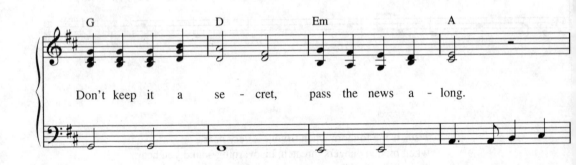

Don't keep it a se - cret, pass the news a - long.

Je - sus is the pass - word, pass it on. Pass it on,

pass it on,   un - til   ev - 'ry-bo - dy knows.   Pass it on,

pass it on,   that's the   way the King - dom grows.   Pass it on,

pass it on,   un - til   all the world has heard.   Pass it on,

pass it on,   that Je - sus is Lord.

Words and Music: Paul Field

203 Jesus, I will come with you

Je - sus, I will come with you, I will fol - low

in your way. I will trust you, I will bring you all I have to -

day. Je - sus, you're the way,

Je - sus, you're the truth, Je - sus,

The two halves of the chorus may be sung simultaneously.

to verses last time

you're the life, praise your name! 1. A - name!

Verse

maz-ing grace, how sweet the sound, that could save a wretch like me. I

once was lost but now I'm found, was blind but now I see.

2. Gentle Jesus, meek and mild,
   look upon a little child.
   Pity my simplicity,
   loving him who first loved me.

3. Let us with a gladsome mind,
   praise the Lord for he is kind.
   For his mercies aye endure,
   ever faithful, ever sure.

4. Praise God from whom all blessings flow,
   praise him all creatures here below.
   Praise him above ye heav'nly host,
   praise Father, Son, and Holy Ghost.

Words and Music: Roger Jones arr. Donald Thomson

204 Jesus, Jesus, here I am

Je-sus, Je-sus, here I am;

Je-sus, Je-sus, take my hand.

You give to ev-'ry-one a love that won't end.

Thank you, Je-sus, you're my friend.

Words and Music: Philip Hawthorne

205 Jesus, Jesus, I love you
(You are lovely)

1. Je - sus, Je - sus, I love you, I

love you. Je - sus, Je - sus, I

last time to Coda

1. love you, I love you. *to verse 2*

2. dore you. You are

love - ly; my eyes long to see your face, and see the scars you

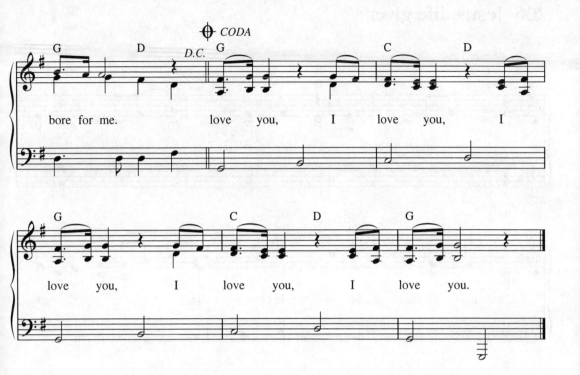

2. Jesus, Jesus, I adore you, I adore you.
   Jesus, Jesus, I adore you, I adore you.

Words and Music: Leon Olguin and Sheryl Olguin

206 Jesus, life giver

Je - sus, life gi - ver. Je - sus, my Sa - viour. Je - sus, Je - sus, Je - sus.

1. You shed your blood on Cal - va - ry. You gave your life for me.

2. I come to you
   to bow my knee.
   You are my Lord and King,

Words and Music: Sue Howson arr. Donald Thomson

207 Jesus' love has got under our skin
(Under our skin)

Je-sus' love has got un-der our skin,

Je-sus' love has got un-der our skin.

Deep-er than col - our oh; rich-er than

cul - ture oh; strong-er than e - mo - tion oh;

wi - der than the o - cean oh. Don't you want to

Words and Music: Graham Kendrick

208 Jesus' love is very wonderful

Words: H.W. Rattle
Music: unknown, arr. Noel Rawsthorne

209 Jesus put this song into our hearts

'Hebrew' style, getting faster
(verse 5 instrumental)

1. Je - sus put this song in - to our hearts,
Je - sus put this song in - to our hearts,
it's a song of joy no one can take a - way, Je - sus put this song
in - to our hearts.

2. Jesus taught us how to live in harmony,
   Jesus taught us how to live in harmony,
   diff'rent faces, diff'rent races, he made us one,
   Jesus taught us how to live in harmony.

3. Jesus taught us how to be a family,
   Jesus taught us how to be a family,
   loving one another with the love that he gives,
   Jesus taught us how to be a family.

4. Jesus turned our sorrow into dancing,
   Jesus turned our sorrow into dancing,
   changed our tears of sadness into rivers of joy,
   Jesus turned our sorrow into a dance.

Words and Music: Graham Kendrick

210 Jesus, reign in me

Je - sus, reign in me, Je - sus, reign in me; take your place with - in my heart and, Je - sus, reign in me.

2. Jesus, you're my King,
   Jesus, you're my King;
   take your place within my heart
   and, Jesus, you're my King.

3. Jesus, live in me,
   Jesus, live in me;
   take your place within my heart
   and, Jesus, live in me.

4. Jesus, forgive me,
   Jesus, forgive me;
   take your place within my heart
   and, Jesus, forgive me.

5. Jesus, I love you,
   Jesus, I love you;
   take your place within my heart
   and, Jesus, I love you.

Words and Music: Chris Jackson

211 Jesus, rock of my salvation
(On this rock)

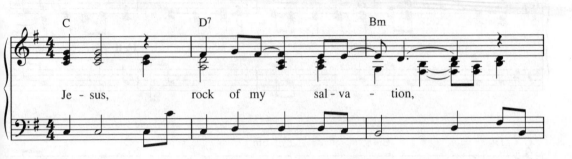

Je - sus,   rock of my   sal - va - tion,

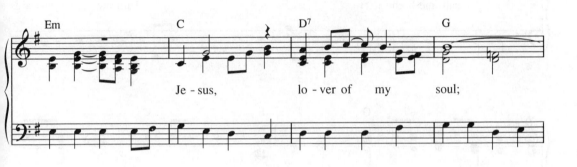

Je - sus,   lo - ver of   my   soul;

you a - lone give life   that lasts   for

e -   ver,   you a - lone

Words and Music: Sue Howson

212 Jesus rode a donkey

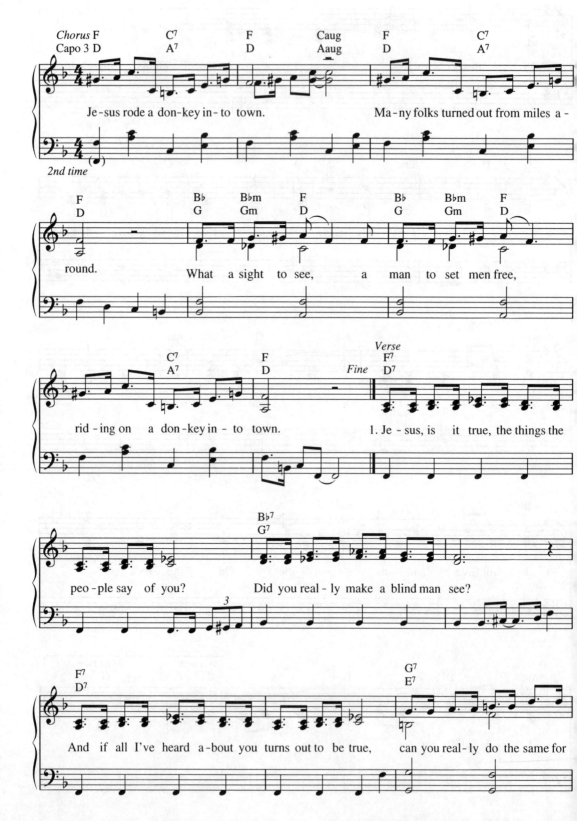

2. Tell me, do you think he'll take the Roman guards by storm?
Do you think he'll show the priests the door?
Wonder if he's pleased by all the shouting from the crowd,
Even by the palms upon the floor.

Words and Music: Roger Jones arr. Donald Thomson

213 Jesus, send me the helper

214 Jesus, thank you for the cross

Je - sus, thank you for the cross, hold-ing no-thing back, you did all your Fa - ther asked. I'll ne - ver know just how it felt as you died, lift - ed high. I know it hurt, I know the pain was more than words could e - ver say. You had a choice,

Words and Music: Mike Burn arr. Donald Thomson

215 Jesus, touch me now

1. Jesus, touch me now, please, I ask you, now. Do your heal-ing work in me, your Spi-rit work-ing ten-der-ly, make me the best that I can be, O, Je-sus, touch me now, O, Je-sus touch me now. use me now.

2. Jesus, use me now,
   please, I ask you, now.
   Do your healing work through me,
   your power working lovingly,
   a useful servant I would be,
   O, Jesus, use me now,
   O, Jesus, use me now.

Words and Music: Capt. Alan Price, CA arr. Gillian Venton
© Copyright 1996 Daybreak Music Ltd, Silverdale Road, Eastbourne,
East Sussex, BN20 7AB, UK. Used by permission.

216 Jesus wants me

2. Jesus still calls his people,
   there's a job to be done;
   no matter who you are
   there's a role for ev'ryone.

3. There's a cost to following,
   of that we may be sure;
   but we'll get back ev'rything we give
   and even more.

Words and Music: Capt. Alan Price, CA arr. Gillian Venton
© Copyright 1996 Daybreak Music, Silverdale Road, Eastbourne,
East Sussex, BN20 7AB, UK. Used by permission.

217 Jesus, we celebrate your victory

1. It was for free - dom that Christ has set us free,
no long - er to be sub - ject to a
yoke of sla - ve - ry; so we're re - joic - ing
in God's vic - to - ry, our hearts re - spond-ing to his
love. life.

2. His Spirit in us releases us from fear,
the way to him is open, with boldness we draw near.
And in his presence our problems disappear;
our hearts responding to his love.

Words and Music: John Gibson

Je - sus, we thank you; Lord, you are here.

Thank you for lov - ing us, as we draw near.

As we draw near, as we draw near.

Words and Music: Capt. Alan Price, CA arr. Donald Thomson

219 Jesus, you are here

2. In our songs of worship
   we lift our voice to you,
   accept the love and thanks we bring
   for all the things you do,
   and we worship you, our Lord.

3. I lift my head up to you
   in expectancy,
   ready to receive your love,
   your gift of grace to me,
   and I worship you, my Lord.

Words and Music: Capt. Alan Price, CA

220 Jesus, you are my King

Calmly, with reverence

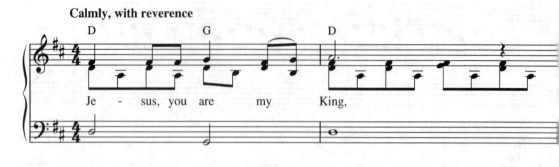

Je - sus, you are my King,

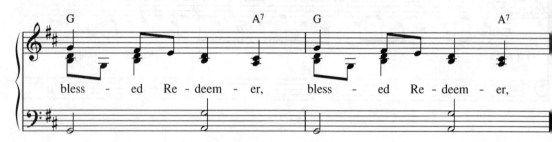

bless - ed Re - deem - er, bless - ed Re - deem - er,

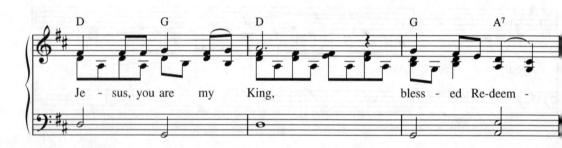

Je - sus, you are my King, bless - ed Re-deem -

er.

2. Jesus, you are my Lord,
beautiful Saviour, beautiful Saviour,
Jesus, you are my Lord,
beautiful Saviour.

3. Jesus, you are my rock,
King of the nations, King of the nations,
Jesus, you are my rock,
King of the nations.

Words and Music: Pete Simpson

221 Jesus, you gave everything

Je - sus, you gave ev – 'ry - thing for me, and I want to learn to give to you through the way I use my time, my mo - ney and my tal - ents; help me give them all to please you.

Words and Music: Bev Gammon

222 Jesus, you're the King

Je - sus, you're the King, Lord of ev - 'ry - thing. You are God's Son, you're num - ber one, and that is why we sing.

1. Je - sus, you came down from heav'n to the earth to serve us. You died but then you rose a - gain. Glo - ry, hal - le - lu - ia!

2. Help me to be more like you;
   ev'ry day I need you.
   I want to praise your name right now.
   Here we go again!

Words and Music: Paul Crouch and David Mudie
© Copyright 1990 Daybreak Music Ltd, Silverdale Road, Eastbourne,
East Sussex, BN20 7AB, UK. Used by permission.

223 Just as the Father sent you

Words and Music: Capt. Alan Price, CA arr. D. Coad

224 Keep me close to you

2. When others use bad or dirty words,
   help me to know what to do.
   Stop me if ever I'm tempted
   to do the same thing too.

3. If ever I get in bad places
   with those who would cause me to stray,
   Lord, let your light shine out from me
   or help me to get right away.

Words and Music: Capt. Alan Price, CA arr. Donald Thomson

225 Let me tell you about a baby
(Christmas calypso)

1. Let me tell you a - bout a ba - by, and his fa - mi - ly.
It is writ - ten down in the Bi - ble
so you might be - lieve. Ma - ny men had told
of his com - ing, down through his - to - ry.
Now the time had come for ful - fil - ment of their pro - phe - cy.

2. There was once a young girl called Mary,
   only in her teens.
   She was visited by an angel,
   sent to Galilee.
   And he told her she'd have a baby,
   how she couldn't see.
   Yet it was her will to obey him,
   so it was agreed.

3. Well, in those days Caesar Augustus
   issued a decree,
   and so Mary went with her husband
   where they had to be.
   There was nowhere else but a stable,
   where they both could sleep.
   It was there that she had her baby,
   born for you and me.

Words and Music: Mark and Helen Johnson arr. Donald Thomson

226 Let's celebrate

Let's ce - le - brate and clap our hands, let's

sing for joy and dance a -round; let's raise our hands and

praise his name for Je - sus is our King.

Al - le - lu - ia.

Words and Music: Jim Aldwinckle and Ron Sivers
© Copyright Wellingborough Christian Centre, St John Street, Wellingborough,
Northamptonshire, NN8 4LG, UK. Used by permission.

227 Let's get fit

2. It's time to increase the pace now,
   it's time for us all to race now,
   let's step into his grace now,
   and let's get fit.
   Let all creation sing now,
   he's giving us a time of spring now,
   it's time for us all to win now,
   so let's get fit.

Words and Music: Kath Fathers

228 Let's sing and make music to the Lord
(Give thanks)

1. Let's sing and make mu-sic to the Lord. Let's sing and make mu-sic to the Lord. Give thanks to God the Fa-ther, give thanks to Je-sus his Son. Give thanks to God the Fa-ther, give thanks to Je-sus his Son.

2. Let's praise and make music to the Lord.
Let's praise and make music to the Lord.
Give thanks to God the Father,
give thanks to Jesus his Son.
Give thanks to God the Father,
give thanks to Jesus his Son.

Words and Music: Yvonne Scott

229 Let us run with determination

Words and Music: Chris Jackson

230 Let us sing and praise God
(Hallelujah dance song)

1. Let us sing and praise God for all that he has done, for
lov - ing us so much in send - ing his Son. Let us
sing and let him know, let our prai - ses o - ver - flow, let us
sing, let us shout, hal - le - lu - jah!

2. Let us sing and praise God, let him know just how we feel,
by our words and actions, show our love for him is real.
Let us laugh, take a chance, lift our feet and have a dance,
as we sing, as we shout, hallelujah!

3. Let us pray to the Lord that we'll never let him down,
never let temptation cause our friendship to break down.
Holy Spirit come right in and keep us close to him,
always sing, always shout, hallelujah!

Words and Music: Capt. Alan Price, CA arr. Chris Hinkins

© Copyright 1992 Daybreak Music Ltd, Silverdale Road, Eastbourne,
East Sussex, BN20 7BA, UK. Used by permission.

231 Let your love shine through
(Hand in hand)

Lyrics:

1. Let your love shine through these eyes of mine, let me be a light for you each day. Let your love show to ev-'ry-one I know, help me learn to fol-low in your way.

Chorus

Hand in hand for e - ver, ne - ver let me go, sure e -

nough to - ge - ther wher - e - ver I may go. No

mat – ter where life leads, give me faith to see your

plan, so ev - 'ry step I take, I take with you

hand in hand.

2. Jesus, you are my bright shining star,
   your word and your Spirit lead me on.
   The best I can do is a life shared with you,
   only in your love can I be strong.

Words and Music: Paul Field

232 Life is like a big wide ocean

Life is like a big wide o-cean and we're sail-ing the o - cean with Je-sus our friend. The jour-ney is long and the wea-ther un-cer - tain, but Je-sus is with us from be - gin-ning to end. Je-sus knows the best course to sail. Let's ask him to guide us. Je - sus knows the best course to sail, with the Ho - ly Spi - rit com-pass in - side us! Wa! wa! wa! wa!

Words and Music: Capt. Alan Price, CA arr. Gillian Venton
© Copyright 1996 Daybreak Music Ltd, Silverdale Road, Eastbourne,
East Sussex, BN20 7AB, UK. Used by permission.

233 Lift his name high

Words and Music: Doug Horley arr. Donald Thomson

234 Lord, I lift your name on high
(You came from heaven to earth)

Lord, I lift your name on high;

Lord, I love to sing your prai - ses.

I'm so glad you're in my life;

I'm so glad you came to save us.

Chorus

You came from hea-ven to earth to show the way,

from the earth to the cross, my debt to pay;

from the cross to the grave, from the grave to the sky,

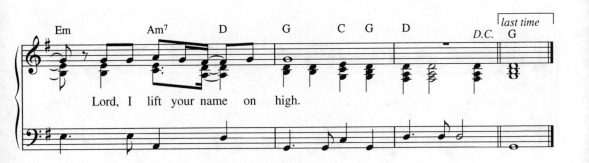

Lord, I lift your name on high.

Words and Music: Rick Founds

235 Lord, I want to be in your family

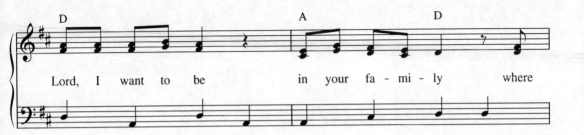

Lord, I want to be in your fa - mi - ly where

to repeat

last time

I can feel so safe and warm. 2. Now I warm.

2. Now I know there might be times that I will let you down.
the things I say might not bless your name.
But Lord, I know you'll never let me go,
yesterday, today, for ever, you're the same.

Words and Music: Iain Craig

236 Lord, look into my heart

Words and Music: Chris Jackson

237 Lord, the light of your love
(Shine, Jesus, shine)

Majestic and steady

Verse

1. Lord, the light of your love is shin - ing,

in the midst of the dark - ness, shin - ing; Je - sus, Light of the

World, shine up - on us, set us free by the truth you now bring us.

Shine on me, shine on me.

Chorus

Shine, Je - sus, shine,   fill this land with the Fa - ther's glo - ry;
Flow, ri - ver, flow,   flood the na - tions with grace and mer - cy;

1.

blaze, Spi - rit, blaze,   set our hearts on   fire.
send forth your word,   Lord, and

2.   *last time*

let there be light.

2. Lord, I come to your awesome presence,
   from the shadows into your radiance;
   by the blood I may enter your brightness,
   search me, try me, consume all my darkness.
   Shine on me, shine on me.

3. As we gaze on your kingly brightness,
   so our faces display your likeness,
   ever changing from glory to glory;
   mirrored here may our lives tell your story.
   Shine on me, shine on me.

   (Chorus twice to end)

Words and Music: Graham Kendrick

238 Lord, we cry

Lord, we cry out to you.
Lord, we cry out to you. Have
mer - cy, have mer - cy on
us.

2. Open our eyes to see.
   Open our eyes to see.
   We want to see,
   we want to see you.

3. Lord, we will follow you.
   Lord, we will follow you.
   We'll follow you,
   we'll follow in the way of truth.

Words and Music: Ken McGreavy and Wes Sutton arr. Donald Thomson

239 Lord, we give you praise

Words and Music: Mick Ray

240 Lord, we lift you high

to next verse *to bridge*

high. 2. Lord, we lift you You are

God, Je - sus the Lord of all, we place you a -

bove all else. So shine through me and keep

draw-ing the world to your heart. Lord, we lift you

2. Lord, we lift you high
   when we're good and kind;
   when we turn from wrong
   and we do what's right,
   that is how we lift you up.
   Lord, we lift you high
   when we shine like stars;
   when we tell our friends
   just how good you are,
   that is how we lift you up.

Words and Music: Judy Bailey arr. Donald Thomson

241 Lord, we've come to worship you

With a gentle rhythm

Lord, we've come to wor-ship you, Lord, we've come to praise; Lord, we've come to wor-ship you in oh so ma-ny ways. Some of us shout and some of us sing, and some of us whis-per the praise we bring; but, Lord, we all are ga-ther-ing to give to you our praise.

Words and Music: Ian Smale

242 Lord, you gave me joy in my heart

Happily

1. Lord, you gave me joy in my heart, joy in my heart al-ways, and it's you I want to praise. 2. Lord, you gave me peace in my mind, peace in my mind al-ways;

(after verse 2 add 1 bar each verse)

peace in my mind joy in my heart, and it's you I want to praise.

3. Lord, you gave me a song in my mouth . . .

4. Lord, you gave me hands that will clap . . .

5. Lord, you gave me feet that can dance . . .

6. Lord, you gave me a love for others . . .

243 Lord, you put a tongue in my mouth

With pace

G

1. Lord, you put a tongue in my mouth and I want to sing to you.

D

Lord, you put a tongue in my mouth and I want to sing to you.

G

Lord, you put a tongue in my mouth and I want to

sing on - ly to you. Lord Je - sus,

free us in our praise; Lord

Je - sus, free us in our

praise.

1st and 2nd times   *last time*

2. Lord, you put some hands on my arms
   which I want to raise to you . . .

3. Lord, you put some feet on my legs
   and I want to dance to you . . .

Words and Music: Ian Smale

244 Lord, you've promised through you Son
(Lord, forgive us)

Lord, you've pro-mised, through your Son, you'll for-give the wrongs we've done; we con-fess them, ev-'ry one, please, dear Lord, for-give us.

1. Things we've done and things we've said, we re-gret the hurt they spread. Lord, we're sor-ry. Lord,

we're sor - ry. we re - ceive your

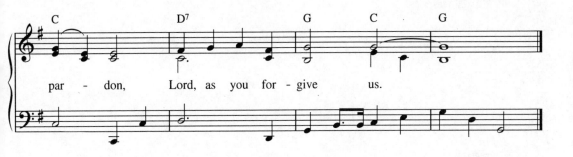

par - don, Lord, as you for - give us.

2. Sinful and unkind thoughts too,
   all of these are known to you.
   Lord, we're sorry,
   Lord, we're sorry.

3. And the things we've left undone,
   words and deeds we should have done.
   Lord, we're sorry,
   Lord, we're sorry.

Words and Music: Capt. Alan Price, CA arr. Norman Warren

245 Love, love your enemies

Love, love your e-ne-mies, do good to those who hate you;

love, love your e-ne-mies, do good to those who hate you. For-

give o-thers and God will for-give you, give to o-thers and

God will give back; for-give o-thers and God will for-give you,

give to o-thers and God will give back to you.

Words and Music: Derek Rowlinson

246 Majesty

Ma - jes - ty, wor - ship his ma - jes - ty,

un - to Je - sus be glo - ry, hon - our and praise.

Ma - jes - ty, king-dom au -

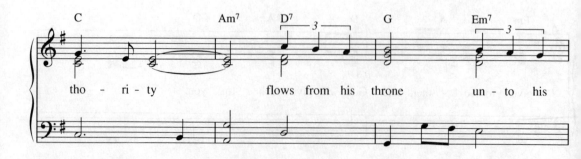

tho - ri - ty flows from his throne un - to his

Words and Music: Jack W. Hayford

247 Make a joyful noise

Make a joy-ful noise un-to the Lord, all the earth,
make a joy-ful noise un-to the Lord.

Lord. Make a loud noise, and re-
joice, sing prai - ses, make a joy-ful noise un-to the
Lord. Make a Lord.

At this point, make a quick sound (clap, whistle, shout, etc.)

This song may be sung as a round, new voices entering as indicated.

Words and Music: Jimmy and Carol Owens

248 Make me a channel of your peace

sole, to be un-der-stood, as to un-der-stand, to be loved, as to love with all my soul.

2. Make me a channel of your peace.
   Where there's despair in life, let me bring hope.
   Where there is darkness, only light,
   and where there's sadness, ever joy.

3. Make me a channel of your peace.
   It is in pardoning that we are pardoned,
   in giving of ourselves that we receive,
   and in dying that we're born to eternal life.

Dedicated to Mrs Frances Tracy

Words and Music: Sebastian Temple, based on the Prayer of St Francis

249 Make way, make way

1. Make way, make way, for Christ the King in splen - dour ar-rives; fling wide the gates and wel - come him in - to your lives. Make

(echo) (make way,) (make way,) (for the King of kings;)
way, make way, for the King of kings; make

(make way,) (make way,)
way, make way, and let his king - dom in!

2. He comes the broken hearts to heal,
   the pris'ners to free;
   the deaf shall hear, the lame shall dance,
   the blind shall see.

3. And those who mourn with heavy hearts,
   who weep and sigh,
   with laughter, joy and royal crown
   he'll beautify.

4. We call you now to worship him
   as Lord of all,
   to have no gods before him,
   their thrones must fall.

Words and Music: Graham Kendrick

250 Mercy is falling

Mer-cy is fall - ing, is fall - ing, is fall - ing, mer-cy it falls like the sweet spring rain. Mer-cy is fall - ing, is fall - ing all o - ver me. Hey O, I re-ceive your mer-cy. Hey O, I re-ceive your grace. Hey O, I will dance for e - ver-more.

Words and Music: David Ruis

251 Midnight

In a steady swing style

Verse Dm / Capo 3 Bm

1. Mid - night, there's the strang - est fee - ling in the
   Star - light, break - ing through the dark - ness in the

air to - night; there's some-thing go - ing on but I can't
dead of night, il - lu - mi - nates the path that takes you

make it out, I won - der what it's all a - bout?
out of sight, and all the way to Beth - le - hem.

To - night's e - vents

were planned in hea - ven, the great - est sto -

- ry e-ver penned. Hea - ven and earth have come to-ge - ther, and life has come to Beth.- le - hem.

to continue

D.C. to next verse
or D.S. for extra chorus

last time

2. Angels – taking care of things that only they can do,
   are waiting in the wings to bring the joyful news,
   it's going to turn the world around.
   Strangers – having made arrangements for a night or two,
   have found accommodation in the crowded rooms.
   The house is packed in Bethlehem.

3. Shepherds – minding their own business looking after things,
   are startled by an unexpected happening,
   as angel choirs appear to them.
   Wise men – taking charts and telescopes and compasses,
   investigate the star that takes them travelling,
   until they come to Bethlehem.

Words and Music: Mark and Helen Johnson

252 Mind the gap
(The bridge)

Mind the gap! (I tell you). Mind the gap! (don't fall down). Mind the gap! (I heard him say). You need to get a-cross (but how?). You need to get a-cross (just look!). You need to get a-cross o-ver the bridge. bridge. 1. Long a-go, when the world be-gan, we and God were best of friends,

2. Think of things that we all do and say, when we're selfish and unkind.
   Broken objects we can stick and mend, but not our broken hearts and lives.
   Don't give up or feel despair, whether girl or boy, woman or man.
   God's the best friend we could have; here's the story of his rescue plan.

3. It was just two thousand years ago, Jesus Christ was born on earth;
   he was so amazing, time was changed, it began again from Jesus' birth!
   He said, 'Look! I am the bridge!' and the price he paid for wood and nails
   was his life, but the price was right, for the Cross shows love that never fails.

Words and Music: Robyn Barnett arr. Donald Thomson

253 Mister Cow

1. Mis-ter Cow, how do you say to the Lord, 'I love you?'
Mis-ter Cow, how do you say to the Lord, 'I love you?' 'Well I
stand a-round in the field all day, and it gives me plen-ty of time to say:
Moo! Moo! Moo!'

2. Mister Sheep . . .
   'Well I stand around in the field all day . . .
   Baa! Baa! Baa!'

3. Mister Horse . . .
   'Well I stand around in the field all day . . .
   Neigh! Neigh! Neigh!'

4. Mister Chicken . . .
   'Well I peck around in the yard all day . . .
   Cluck! Cluck! Cluck!'

5. Mister Pig . . .
   'Well I roll around in the mud all day . . .
   Oink! Oink! Oink!'

6. Mister Fish . . .
   'Well I swim around in the pond all day . . .
   Pop! Pop! Pop!'

7. Mister Duck . . .
   'Well I swim around in the pond all day . . .
   Quack! Quack! Quack!'

Words and Music: Julia Plaut

254 Moses went down to see Pharoah
(The last word)

1. Moses went down to see Pharaoh, he said, 'Let my people go'. Moses went down to see Pharaoh, all Pharaoh could say was 'no'. Moses turned his staff to a snake, oh, he turned the Nile into blood. Pharaoh be fair, oh let my people go.' Pharaoh said 'no' when he shouldn't

2. Moses went down to see Pharaoh,
   Pharaoh not in a good mood.
   He told Moses to 'hop it', and that
   'Moses, you're going to get sued'.
   Moses gave him a flea in the ear,
   bugged him, got under his skin.
   Pharaoh he cried, 'Pass the insecticide'.
   Moses laughed, there were no flies on him.

3. Moses went down to see Pharaoh,
   Pharaoh was not very pleased.
   Pharaoh he came to boiling point,
   when Egypt got mad cow disease.
   But God, through Moses, wasn't finished
   and, afflicted with terrible sores,
   Pharaoh was to see God was bigger than he,
   and that it never rains, it just pours.

4. Moses went down to see Pharaoh,
   'Hail, Pharaoh,' he said, tongue in cheek.
   'The locusts are coming to finish the job
   and devour all there is left to eat.
   Then darkness will cover the land oh,
   just because you couldn't see.
   Your firstborn will die, due to your stubborn pride,
   and my people they will be set free.

Words and Music: Jim Bailey arr. Donald Thomson

255 My God is so big

2. He's called you to live for him ev'ry day
   in all that you say and you do . . .

Words and Music: Traditional
This arrangement © Copyright 1998 Kevin Mayhew Ltd.

256 My God shall supply all my needs

My God shall sup-ply all my needs, my
God shall sup-ply all my needs, my
God shall sup-ply all my needs 'cause it
says so in the Bi - ble. 'Cause it

says   so   (where?)   in   the   book   that   came   from   heav'n,   'cause   it

says   so   (where?)   I-sai-ah   fif-ty-eight   e-lev'n.   My

God   shall   sup-ply   all   my   needs,   'cause   it

says   so   in   the   Bi-ble.

Words and Music: Ian Smale

257 My Jesus, my Saviour
(Shout to the Lord)

let us sing   pow - er and ma   -   jes - ty, praise

of your hands.   For   e - ver I'll love   you, for e -

to the King.   Moun-tains bow down   and the seas

- ver I'll stand.   No - thing com - pares   to the pro -

1. will roar   at the sound   of your name.

2. - mise I have in you.

Words and Music: Darlene Zschech

258 My lips shall praise you
(Restorer of my soul)

night   to   bright - est   day;   you   are   the   re -

sto - rer   of   my   soul.

2. Love that conquers ev'ry fear,
   in the midst of trouble you draw near;
   you are the restorer of my soul.

3. You're the source of happiness,
   bringing peace when I am in distress;
   you are the restorer of my soul.

Words and Music: Noel and Tricia Richards

259 My rock

260 Na, na, na, na, na
(There's a place)

Na na na na na, na na na na na na na na.

Chorus

There's a place wait-ing for me, a place that's good to be, I know, 'cos Je - sus said it! There's a place wait-ing for me, a place that's good to be, I know, 'cos

Words and Music: Capt. Alan Price, CA arr. Donald Thomson.

261 Nobody liked Zacchaeus
(Zacchaeus)

(4.)

Je-sus loves peo-ple like you! Oh, you'd bet-ter get off your back, Zack, you'd bet-ter come down from the tree; no mat-ter what o-thers may think of you, to Je-sus you're spe-cial, you see!

2. Now Zack, he heard about Jesus,
   he climbed up a tree for a view;
   said Jesus, 'I'm coming to your house today;
   Zacchaeus, I'm talking to you!'

3. Because of the visit of Jesus,
   Zacchaeus became someone new;
   he gave four times as much as he'd cheated,
   and half of his wealth away, too!

4. You might not be quite like Zacchaeus,
   but sometimes you may feel quite blue.
   the Bible is clear about one thing;
   Jesus loves people like you!

Final Chorus:
   Oh, you'd better get off your back, Whack,
   you'd better just listen to me;
   no matter what others may think of you,
   to Jesus you're special, you see!

Words and Music: Capt. Alan Price, CA

262 Now I belong to Jesus

Words and Music: Capt. Alan Price, CA

263 Obey the maker's instructions

1. So you can buy a mo-del of your fav-'rite clas-sic car, with-out read-ing in-struc – tions you put it to-ge-ther so far; but when you think you're fin – ished you find a lit-tle ex-tra bit, it's the dri-ver of the car but now he just won't fit. O-bey the ma-ker's in-struc-

2. Say that you read the Bible
to see what God has said,
and you find instructions
and store them in your head;
but when you find that you're tempted
to doing things the wrong way,
instructions mean nothing
unless you do what they say.

Words and Music: Sammy Horner arr. Donald Thomson

264 Oh, I'm fighting

Words and Music: Mike Burn

265 Oh, it's so good to know
(Oh, it's good to know you)

Oh, it's so good to know, oh, it's so good.

Oh, it's so good to know Je - sus loves me.

me. He loves me so much, he came to earth for me. He

loves me so much, that he died for me. But he came back to life a-gain in

Words and Music: Steve Burnhope

266 Oh! Oh! Oh! how good is the Lord

With a swing

Oh! Oh! Oh! how good is the Lord, Oh! Oh! Oh! how good is the Lord, Oh! Oh! Oh! how good is the Lord, I ne-ver will for-get what he has done for me.

1. He gives me sal-va-tion, how good is the Lord, he gives me sal-va-tion, how good is the Lord, he gives me sal-va-tion, how

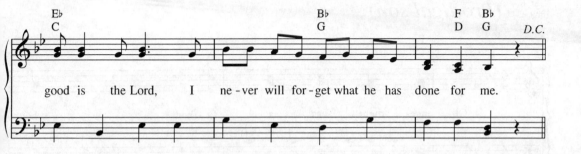

good is the Lord, I ne-ver will for-get what he has done for me.

2. He gives me his blessings, how good is the Lord,
   he gives me his blessings, how good is the Lord,
   he gives me his blessings, how good is the Lord,
   I never will forget what he has done for me.

3. He gives me his Spirit, how good is the Lord,
   he gives me his Spirit, how good is the Lord,
   he gives me his Spirit, how good is the Lord,
   I never will forget what he has done for me.

4. He gives me his healing, how good is the Lord,
   he gives me his healing, how good is the Lord,
   he gives me his healing, how good is the Lord,
   I never will forget what he has done for me.

5. He gives me his glory, how good is the Lord,
   he gives me his glory, how good is the Lord,
   he gives me his glory, how good is the Lord,
   I never will forget what he has done for me.

Other verses may be added as appropriate

Words: Unknown
Music: Unknown arr. Noel Rawsthorne

267 Oh, once there was a father
(Prodigal son)

1. Oh, once there was a father, who had two sons at home. The young one wan-ted mo-ney, so he could start to roam.

Lost! Lost! Lost and found! That's what the Bi-ble said! Lost! Lost! Lost and found! The

son   back   from the   dead.   2. He   dead.

2. He left home one bright morning,
    he said, 'I must be free!
    I'll go to the far country,
    there's marv'lous sights to see!

3. He started spending money
    on women, wine and song;
    but this great time of plenty,
    it didn't last too long!

4. He soon found he was starving,
    the pigs he had to feed;
    when he was back with father,
    he never had a need!

5. He started back to father,
    ashamed and all alone;
    but father saw him coming,
    and welcomed him back home.

Words and Music: Roger Jones arr. Donald Thomson

268 Oh, the Lord is good

Lord is good, so good, so good; so kind, so kind; give him

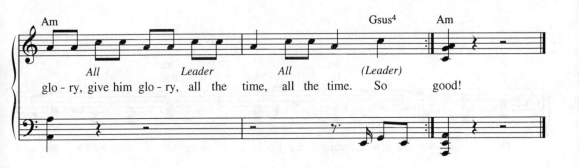

glo - ry, give him glo - ry, all the time, all the time. So good!

2. *Leader* We want to hear the children say:
   All   oh, the Lord is good.
   Leader We want to hear you say:
   All   the Lord is good.
   Leader We want to hear you loud and strong:
   All   oh, the Lord is good.
   Leader We want to hear you shout:
   All   the Lord is good!

3. *Leader* We want to hear the brothers say:
   All   oh, the Lord is good.
   Leader We want to hear you say:
   All   the Lord is good.
   Leader We want to hear the sisters say:
   All   oh, the Lord is good.
   Leader We want to hear you say:
   All   the Lord is good.

4. *Leader* The younger to the older say:
   Younger oh, the Lord is good.
   Leader We want to hear you say:
   Younger the Lord is good.
   Leader Older to the younger say:
   Older   oh, the Lord is good.
   Leader We want to hear you say:
   Older   the Lord is good!

5. *Leader* Let ev'ry generation say:
   All   oh, the Lord is good.
   Leader We want to hear you say:
   All   the Lord is good,
   Leader so good,
   All   so good;
   Leader so kind,
   All   so kind;
   Leader give him glory,
   All   give him glory,
   Leader all the time,
   All   all the time.
   Leader So good . . .

Words and Music: Graham Kendrick

269 Oi, oi, we are gonna praise the Lord

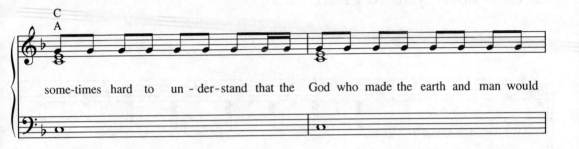

some-times hard to un-der-stand that the God who made the earth and man would

point a fin-ger down from hea-ven and shout: 'Hey you! I love you. Hey

you! I love you. Hey you, you! I love you.' – but it's true!

Words and Music: Doug Horley

270 O Lord, you're great

2. O Lord, you're great, you are so powerful,
   you hold the mighty universe in your hand, hand, hand.
   O Lord, you're great, you are so beautiful,
   you've poured out your love on this undeserving land.

Words and Music: Ian Smale

271 On Calvary's tree

On Cal-v'ry's tree he died for me, that I his love might know. To set me free he died for me, that's why I love him so.

Words: A. W. Edsor
Music: A. E. Walton adapted by A. W. Edsor
© Copyright Kingsway's Thankyou Music, P.O. Box 75, Eastbourne,
East Sussex, BN23 6NW, UK. Used by permission.

272 Once there was a house
(Busy little house)

Gently

1. Once there was a house, a bu - sy lit - tle house, and
(v.2+7) this is all a - bout (v.3) the bu - sy lit - tle house.

2. Jesus Christ had come, teaching ev'ryone,
   so ev'ryone has run to the busy little house.

3. Ev'ryone was there, you couldn't find a chair,
   in fact you had to fight for air in the busy little house.

4. A man who couldn't walk was carried to the spot,
   but the place was chock-a-block in the busy little house.

5. Whatever shall we do, whatever shall we do?
   We'll never get him through into the busy little house.

6. We'll open up the roof, we'll open up the roof,
   and then we'll put him through into the busy little house.

7. Then Jesus turned his eyes, and saw to his surprise
   the man coming from the skies into the busy little house.

8. Then Jesus turned and said, 'Get up and take your bed,
   and run along instead from the busy little house.'

Words and Music: Ian White

273 One more step along the world I go

1. One more step a-long the world I go, one more step a-long the world I go. From the old things to the new, keep me tra-vel-ling a-long with you. And it's from the old I tra-vel to the new, keep me tra-vel-ling a-long with you.

2. Round the corners of the world I turn,
more and more about the world I learn.
All the new things that I see
you'll be looking at along with me.

3. As I travel through the bad and good,
keep me travelling the way I should.
Where I see no way to go,
you'll be telling me the way, I know.

4. Give me courage when the world is rough,
keep me loving though the world is tough.
Leap and sing in all I do,
keep me travelling along with you.

5. You are older than the world can be,
you are younger than the life in me.
Ever old and ever new,
keep me travelling along with you.

Words and Music: Sydney Carter

274 One, two, three, Jesus loves me

Happily

Chorus

One, two, three, Je-sus loves me. One, two, Je-sus loves you.

Verses

1. Three, four, he loves you more than you've e - ver been loved be - fore.

2. Five, six, seven, we're go - ing to heav'n. Eight, nine, it's tru - ly di - vine.

to repeat whole hymn

3. Nine, ten, it's time to end; but in - stead we'll sing it a - gain.

to end

there's no time to sing it a - gain.

Words and Music: Lisa Mazak arr. Donald Thomson

275 Only one of me, only one of you
(So great)

1. On-ly one of me, on-ly one of you, on-ly one of ev-'ry-one, in-cre-di-ble but true. Mil-lions of us all, none of us the same, but God knows ev-'ry sin-gle face and ev-'ry sin-gle name. Be-cause he's so great, on-ly God can do it, so great, that's

why we sing. So great, I wish ev-'ry-bo - dy knew it,

so great, that's why we wor - ship him.

2. Ev'ry thought I think,
   ev'ry prayer I pray,
   ev'ry cry I cry to him and ev'rything I say,
   in a world that's full of words
   that swirl in space and time,
   God's tuned in to all of them,
   he knows which ones are mine.

Words: Judy MacKenzie Dunn
Music: Paul Field

276 On my bed I remember you
(I remember you)

1. On my bed I re-mem-ber you, I re-mem-ber you, O God. On my bed I re-mem-ber you, you are my help. And I will praise you as long as I live, and I will lift up my hands. And I will praise you as long as I live, and I will lift up my hands.

2. When I wake I remember you,
   I remember you, O God.
   When I wake I remember you,
   you are my help.

3. When I eat I remember you,
   I remember you, O God.
   when I eat I remember you,
   You are my help.

4. When I play I remember you,
   I remember you, O God.
   When I play I remember you,
   You are my help.

Words and Music: Yvonne Scott

277 On my tiptoes I am tall

On my tip -toes I am tall, when I crouch down I am so small, I

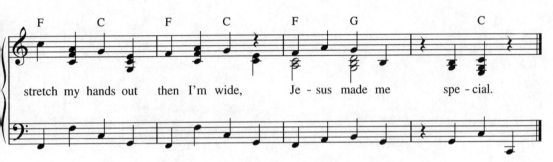

stretch my hands out then I'm wide, Je - sus made me spe - cial.

2. Jesus loves me when I'm tall,
   Jesus loves me when I'm small,
   Jesus loves me when I'm wide,
   Jesus made me special.

3. S - P - E - C - I - A - L,
   S - P - E - C - I - A - L,
   S - P - E - C - I - A - L,
   Jesus made me special.

Words and Music: Ian Smale

278 Open our eyes, Lord

Words and Music: Robert Cull arr. Donald Thomson

279 Over the mountains and the sea
(I could sing of your love for ever)

O-ver the moun-tains and the sea your ri-ver runs with love for me,

and I will o-pen up my heart and let the Heal-er set me free.

I'm hap-py to be in the truth, and I will dai-ly lift my hands,

for I will al-ways sing of when your love came down.

Chorus

I could sing of your love for e-ver, I could sing of your love

Words and Music: Martin Smith

280 People brought children to Jesus

Peo - ple brought child - ren to Je - sus, to
Je - sus, to Je - sus; peo - ple brought child - ren to
Je - sus, to be touched by him.

2. But the disciples tried to stop them,
   to stop them, to stop them;
   but the disciples tried to stop them,
   but they got it wrong!

3. Jesus was angry and he shouted,
   he shouted, he shouted!
   Jesus was angry and he shouted,
   'Let them come to me!'

4. Jesus took the children in his arms,
   in his arms, in his arms;
   Jesus took the children in his arms,
   gave them each a hug!

5. Jesus, please, I ask you, will you hug me too,
   hug me too, hug me too?
   Jesus, please, I ask you, will you hug me too,
   for I am your child!

6. Hallelujah, hallelujah, hallelu!
   Hallelu, hallelu!
   Hallelujah, hallelujah, hallelu!
   Jesus loves me!

Words and Music: Capt. Alan Price, CA arr. Donald Thomson
© Copyright 1998 Daybreak Music Ltd, Silverdale Road, Eastbourne,
East Sussex, BN20 7AB, UK. Used by permission.

281 Peter and John went to pray
(Silver and gold)

Peter and John went to pray, they met a lame man on the way. He
asked for alms and held out his palms, and this is what Peter did say:
'Silver and gold have I none, but such as I have I give you; in the
name of Jesus Christ of Nazareth, rise up and walk!' He went
walking and leaping and praising God, walking and leaping and praising God. 'In the
name of Jesus Christ of Nazareth, rise up and walk.'

Words and Music: Unknown arr. Donald Thomson
This arrangement © Copyright 1999 Kevin Mayhew Ltd.

282 Please fill me, Lord

2. Lord, I want to live for you,
   live the way you want me to,
   do the things that make you glad,
   not the things that make you sad.

Words and Music: Capt. Alan Price, CA arr. Donald Thomson

283 Praise God from whom all blessings flow

Words and Music: Andy Piercy and Dave Clifton arr. Alison Berry

284 Praise him on the trumpet

Words and Music: John Kennett

285 Pray at all times

Words and Music: Mike Burn

286 Prayer is like a telephone
(Prayer phone)

Words and Music: Paul Crouch and David Mudie arr. Donald Thomson

287 Riding high and low
(Riding high)

Verse Dm Am Dm C F
Capo 5 Am Em Am G C

1. Rid - ing high and low, look - ing for a king,

Gm Dm Gm Am Dm
Dm Am Dm Em Am

rid - ing o - ver de - serts, with the gifts we bring.

Am Dm Gm Dm
Chorus Em Am Dm Am

Frank - in - cense and myrrh, gold we bring to him,

Gm Dm Gm Am Dm D
Dm Am Dm Em Am A

to verses *last time*

these are what we'll give and our hearts to him.

2. Over mountains high,
   over deserts dry,
   on to find this baby,
   looking in the sky!

3. On we go to Herod,
   but he'll turn so green,
   when we tell of Jesus,
   and the star we've seen.

4. We are nearly there,
   might get there today;
   star is still above us
   showing us the way.

Words and Music: Roger Jones arr. Donald Thomson

288 Rise, and shine
(Arky, arky song)

Chorus

Rise, and shine, and give God the glo-ry, glo-ry. Rise, and shine, and

give God the glo-ry, glo-ry. Rise, and shine, and give God the glo-ry, glo-ry,

Fine *Verse*

child-ren of the Lord. 1. The Lord said to No - ah: 'There's

gon-na be a flood-y, flood-y.' Lord said to No - ah: 'There's gon-na be a flood-y, flood-y.

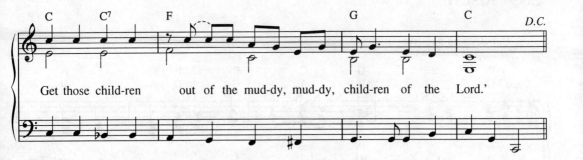

Get those child-ren out of the mud-dy, mud-dy, child-ren of the Lord.'

2. The Lord told Noah to build him an arky, arky,
   Lord told Noah to build him an arky, arky.
   Build it out of gopher barky, barky,
   children of the Lord.

3. The animals, the animals, they came on, by twosies, twosies,
   animals, the animals, they came on, by twosies, twosies.
   Elephants and kangaroosies, 'roosies,
   children of the Lord.

4. It rained and poured for forty daysies, daysies,
   rained and poured for forty daysies, daysies.
   Almost drove those animals crazies, crazies,
   children of the Lord.

5. The sun came out and dried up the landy, landy,
   sun came out and dried up the landy, landy.
   Ev'rything was fine and dandy, dandy,
   children of the Lord.

Words and Music: Traditional arr. Donald Thomson

289 Risen!

an-gels came and told them: 'The one you've come to see,

he is-n't here, but you will meet him soon!'

CODA

Ri - sen! Ri - sen! Je - sus is ri - sen!

2. Fearful and excited, amazed by all they'd seen,
   Mary and her friends ran from the tomb:
   finding the disciples together where they'd meet,
   bursting with joy, they ran into the room.

3. Two of the believers, with thoughts about the week,
   walked the road so lonely and confused.
   While they spoke of Jesus, and all he'd come to mean,
   he came along beside them with the news.

4. All of his disciples were terrified to see
   Jesus before them in the room.
   'Why are you so frightened?' he said 'It's really me!
   all of the things I told you have come true!'

Words and Music: Mark and Helen Johnson

290 Safe in the Father's hands

2. Trusting in God, we can be sure
   no matter where life may lead,
   his promises told, he's in control,
   he's ev'rything we need.

Words and Music: Paul Field

291 See him lying on a bed of straw
(Calypso carol)

1. See him ly - ing on a bed of straw, a draugh-ty sta - ble with an

o - pen door. Ma - ry cra - dl - ing the babe she bore: the

Prince of Glo - ry is his name. Oh, now car - ry me to Beth - le-hem, to

see the Lord of love a - gain: just as poor as was the

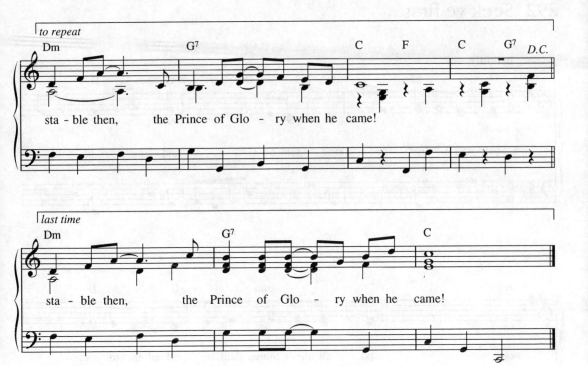

to repeat

Dm   G⁷   C   F   C   G⁷   *D.C.*

sta - ble then,   the Prince of Glo - ry when he came!

last time

Dm   G⁷   C

sta - ble then,   the Prince of Glo - ry when he came!

2. Star of silver, sweep across the skies,
   show where Jesus in the manger lies;
   shepherds, swiftly from your stupor rise
   to see the Saviour of the world!

3. Angels, sing again the song you sang,
   sing the glory of God's gracious plan;
   sing that Bethl'ems little baby can
   be the saviour of us all.

4. Mine are riches from your poverty;
   from your innocence, eternity;
   mine, forgiveness by your death for me,
   child of sorrow for my joy.

Words and Music: Michael Perry

292 Seek ye first

Brightly

Verse

1. Seek ye first the king-dom of God and his right-eous-

ness, and all these things shall be add-ed un-to you,

hal - le - lu, hal - le - lu - jah! Hal - le -

lu - jah! Hal - le - lu - jah! Hal - le -

lu - jah!   Hal - le - lu, hal - le - lu - jah!   lu - jah!

2. You shall not live by bread alone,
   but by every word
   that proceeds from the mouth of God,
   Hallelu, hallelujah!

3. Ask and it shall be given unto you,
   seek and you shall find.
   Knock and it shall be opened unto you,
   hallelu, hallelujah!

4. If the Son shall set you free,
   you shall be free indeed.
   You shall know the truth and the truth shall set you free,
   hallelu, hallelujah!

5. Let your light so shine before men
   that they may see your good works
   and glorify your Father in heaven,
   hallelu, hallelujah!

6. Trust in the Lord with all your heart,
   he shall direct your paths,
   in all your ways acknowledge him,
   hallelu, hallelujah.

Words and Music: Karen Lafferty arr. Donald Thomson

293 Shake a friend's hand
(Ha la la la)

1. Shake a friend's hand, shake a hand next to ya, shake a friend's hand and sing la la;
shake a friend's hand, shake a hand next to ya, shake a friend's hand and
sing, sing a la la la la la la-le-lu-ia, la la la la la-le-lu-ia.
La la la la la la-le-lu-ia, la la la la la-le- lu-

1, 2, 3, 5. ia. *Fine* ia. Don't just stand in your own lit-tle place, reach

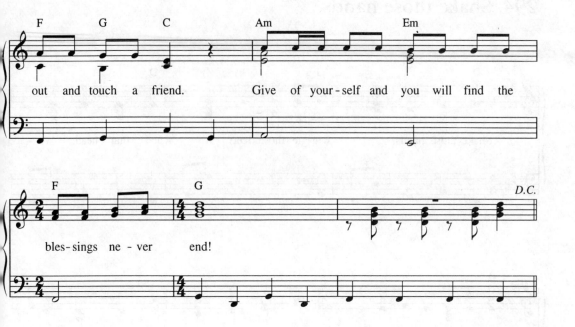

out and touch a friend. Give of your-self and you will find the

bles-sings ne - ver end!

2. Hug a friend's neck, hug a neck next to ya,
   hug a friend's neck and sing la la,
   hug a friend's neck, hug a neck next to ya,
   hug a friend's neck and sing . . .

3. Squeeze a friend's knee, squeeze a knee next to ya,
   squeeze a friend's knee and sing la la,
   squeeze a friend's knee, squeeze a knee next to ya,
   squeeze a friend's knee and sing . . .

4. Scratch a friend's back, scratch a back next to ya,
   scratch a friend's back and sing la la,
   scratch a friend's back, scratch a back next to ya,
   scratch a friend's back and sing . . .

5. Jesus is a friend, he's a friend next to ya,
   Jesus is a friend, so sing la la,
   Jesus is a friend, he's a friend next to ya,
   Jesus is a friend, so sing . . .

Words and Music: David Graham

294 Shake those hands

Shake those hands, wig-gle those feet, nod that head, in case it's still a-sleep. Wake up and praise the Lord, wake up and praise the Lord, wake up and praise the Lord with all of me.

Words and Music: Andrew and Pauline Pearson

295 Shoop shoop

1. Shoop shoop doo - bee doo doo, there's

no - bo-dy who loves me like you do. Shoop shoop doo - bee doo doo,

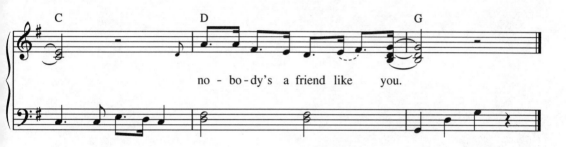

no - bo-dy's a friend like you.

2. Wop bop doobee doo waa,
   we sing your name and shout hallelujah.
   Wop bop doobee doo waa,
   King of kings for ever you are!

3. Shoop shoop doobee doo doo,
   I shout your name and sing hallelujah.
   Shoop shoop doobee doo doo,
   only you can make my life new.

4. Wop bop doobee doo waa,
   we sing your name and shout hallelujah.
   Wop bop doobee doo waa,
   King of kings for ever you are.

5. Shoop shoop doobee doo doo,
   you're ev'rything that ever was true now.
   Shoop shoop doobee doo doo,
   I want to tell my friends about you.

6. Wop bop doobee doo waa,
   we sing your name and shout hallelujah.
   Wop bop doobee doo waa,
   King of kings for ever you are!

Words and Music: Paul Crouch and David Mudie
© Copyright 1995 Daybreak Music Ltd, Silverdale Road, Eastbourne,
East Sussex, BN20 7AB, UK. Used by permission.

296 Sing and shout your praise

Sing and shout your praise to our God, he a-lone is King. He's the ru-ler of the earth, he's the Lord of ev-'ry-thing.

1. He is a migh-ty God, full of ma-jes-ty, glo-ry and ho-nour and pow'r. So come and praise him, shout a-loud, lift his name on high. *(Cheer)*

2. The Lord is merciful, loving and kind;
faithful and gentle is he.
So come and worship him, bow the knee,
magnify his name with me.

Words and Music: Chris Jackson
© Copyright 1998 Powerpack/Learning Curve Music, P.O. Box 421, Hailsham,
East Sussex, BN27 4ZA, UK. Used by permission.

297 Sing a song, sing a joyful song
(Celebrate!)

Bright and bouncy

1. Sing a song, sing a joy-ful song, sing a joy-ful song to

ce-le-brate! Sing a song, sing a joy-ful song, sing a

joy-ful song to ce-le-brate! ce-le-brate!

Je-sus is a-live, you know, he's ri-sen from the dead!

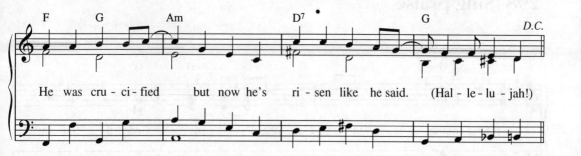

He was cru - ci - fied   but now he's   ri - sen like he said.   (Hal - le - lu - jah!)

2. Clap your hands, clap your hands like this,
   clap your hands like this to celebrate!
   Clap your hands, clap your hands like this,
   clap your hands like this to celebrate!

3. Jump up and down, up and down and around,
   up and down and around to celebrate!
   Jump up and down, up and down and around,
   up and down and around to celebrate!

4. Dance to the beat, to the beat of the drum,
   to the beat of the drum to celebrate!
   Dance to the beat, to the beat of the drum,
   to the beat of the drum to celebrate!

5. Wave your hands, wave your hands in the air,
   wave your hands in the air to celebrate!
   Wave your hands, wave your hands in the air,
   wave your hands in the air to celebrate!

6. Sing a song, sing a joyful song,
   sing a joyful song to celebrate!
   Sing a song, sing a joyful song,
   sing a joyful song to celebrate!

Words and Music: Mark and Helen Johnson arr. Donald Thomson

298 Sing praise

2. Sing praise to God the Father,
   clap your hands and jump for joy.
   He made the world around us,
   and he loves us all.

3. Sing praise to God's Son Jesus,
   clap your hands and jump for joy.
   Wave your arms and turn around.
   He teaches us about the Father,
   and he loves us all.

4. Sing praise to the Holy Spirit,
   clap your hands and jump for joy.
   Wave your arms and jump around,
   stamp your feet and shout hooray.
   He helps us to live like Jesus,
   and he loves us all.

Words and Music: Derek Llewellyn

299 So if you think you're standing firm

So if you think you're stand-ing firm, be care-ful you don't fall; so
if you think you're stand-ing firm, be care-ful you don't fall; so
if you think you're stand-ing firm, be care-ful you don't fall; so
if you think you're stand-ing firm, be care-ful you don't fall.

Words and Music: Ian Smale arr. Donald Thomson

300 So I'll trust in God
(God has got a plan)

2. God was, and God is with me here,
he sent his Son, he takes my fear,
his Spirit lives deep in my heart –
I'm in his plan right from the start.

Words and Music: Nick Harding

301 So I've made up my mind

2. I may be scared
   by the things I hear,
   but Jesus won't
   let me live in fear.

3. I may be scared
   by the things I know,
   but Jesus won't
   ever let me go.

Words and Music: Ian Smale

302 Some people are fat

2. Some people we like, some people we don't,
   but how can we love our neighbour if try we won't?
   God's help is at hand, we just need to ask
   and God the Holy Spirit will help us in the task.

Words and Music: Capt. Alan Price, CA

303 Some people laugh
(What do you do?)

1. Some peo-ple laugh, some peo-ple sing, some peo-ple clap and so they bring their wor-ship to the King of kings. What do you do? What do you do?

2. Some people dance, some bring a word,
   some people cry before the Lord,
   and so they bring their worship to
   the King of kings, the King of kings.

3. Some people march and raise their hands,
   and some are quiet, but understand
   there are many ways of worshipping
   the King of kings, the King of kings.

Words and Music: Sammy Horner
© Copyright 1992 Daybreak Music Ltd, Silverdale Road, Eastbourne,
East Sussex, BN20 7AB, UK. Used by permission.

304 Some things make you angry
(Count to ten)

Verse

1. Some things make you an-gry and some things can make you shout; some-times you can't keep it in, you've got to let it out; but be-fore you lose your tem-per, stop! Count to ten and say a prayer for love.

Chorus

Count to ten and say a prayer, Je-sus al-ways will be there, count to ten and

last time to Coda

talk to him, let him put his love with-in your heart. One, two, three, four, five, six, seven, eight, nine, ten. love with-in, say a prayer for love.

2. Angry words can hurt someone much more than sticks or stones,
   so when you feel your temper rising to the danger zone,
   close your eyes and keep your lips shut tight,
   count to ten and say a prayer for love.

Words and Music: Paul Field arr. Donald Thomson

305 Sometimes in the morning I feel sad
(Wake up and dance for joy)

1. Some-times in the morn-ing I feel sad, sad, sad, so I just ask Je - sus, make my sad heart glad. Wake up and dance for joy, wake up and dance for joy, wake up and dance for joy, first thing in the morn-ing.

2. Sometimes in the morning
   I feel glad, glad, glad,
   so I just praise Jesus
   for the day I'll have.

Words and Music: Chris Mercer

306 So we're marching along
(The Lord's army)

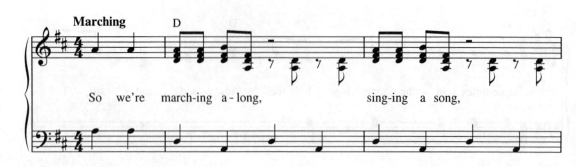

So we're march-ing a-long, sing-ing a song,

we're in the Lord's ar — my. We're

fight-ing for right as we're learn-ing what's wrong, 'cause

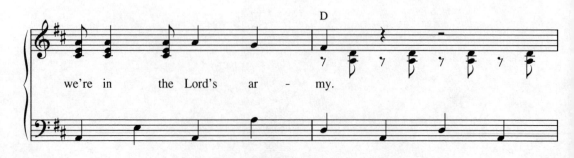

we're in the Lord's ar — my.

He's got the vic - t'ry, so let's real - ly shout,

we're in the Lord's ar - my. We're in the Lord's (yeah),

1.

we're in the Lord's (right), we're in the Lord's ar -

2.

my. we're in the Lord's ar - my.

Words and Music: Ian Smale

307 Speak, Lord

Speak, Lord, I am your ser - vant, I am list -'ning to your voice. Speak, Lord, I am your ser - vant, I am list - 'ning.

Words and Music: Chris Jackson

308 Special agents

men -dous. We're a - gents for Je - sus, the King, 'cos

he's the one who sends us!

D.C.

CODA

Spe-cial a - gents! Spe-cial a - gents!

2. We'll use our eyes to see just where
   God is working around us.
   We'll use our ears to listen, too,
   and act on what he tells us!

Words and Music: Capt. Alan Price, CA

309 Spirit

po-wer is here. I want the weight of your glo-ry to fall on me, so come now Ho-ly me. We wel-come you here, we wel-come you here, we wel-come you here, we need you, we need you. We wel-come you here.

2. I want to know that you're here in this place,
   healing our lives and enlarging our faith.
   I want to know when I leave there's a change in me,
   so come now Holy Spirit . . .

Words and Music: Judy Bailey arr. Donald Thomson

310 Sun and the moon and the starlit sky
(God created them all)

1. Sun and the moon and the star-lit sky, God cre-a-ted them all.

Ri-vers and seas and the o-ceans wide,

he cre-a-ted them all. Fo-rests and fields and the

des-erts dry, God cre-a-ted them all.

Val-leys and foot-hills and moun-tains high. he cre-a-ted them all.

Chorus

God looked down from hea-ven, he was
pleased . . . oh yeah! Ev-'ry-thing was just as it should

1st and 2nd times D.C.

be . . . ah ha! God cre-a-ted the

whole wide world, he cre-a-ted it all!

2. Every creature that moves and breathes,
   God created them all.
   Fliers and swimmers and some with feet,
   he created them all.
   Beautiful flowers and fruitful trees,
   God created them all.
   Every plant that you'll ever see,
   he created them all.

3. Summer and autumn and winter, spring,
   God created them all.
   Each of the changes the seasons bring,
   he created them all.
   Thunder and lightning, the rain and wind,
   God created them all.
   Glorious sunsets and snowy scenes,
   he created them all.

Words and Music: Mark and Helen Johnson

311 S - U - N is shining in the sky
(S - U - N – S - O - N)

S - U - N is shin-ing in the sky, S - U - N is shin-ing

in the sky, bring-ing light, bring-ing light all a-

round. But

S - O - N, the Son who came to die, S - O - N, the Son who

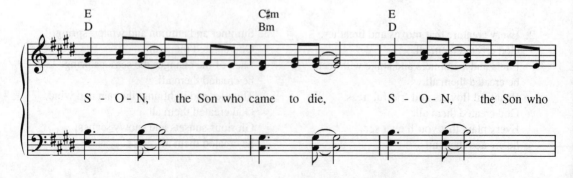

Words and Music: Ian White

312 Teach me to dance

Teach me to dance to the beat of your heart, teach me to move
Teach me to love with your heart of com - pas - sion, teach me to trust

in the pow'r of your Spi - rit, teach me to walk in the light of your pre -
in the word of your pro - mise, teach me to hope in the day of your com -

sence, teach me to dance to the beat of your heart.
ing,

1. You wrote the rhy - thm of life,

cre-a-ted hea-ven and earth, in you is joy with-out mea - sure.

So, like a child in your sight, I dance to see your de-light, for I was made for your

plea - sure, plea - sure.

2. Let all my movements express
   a heart that loves to say 'yes',
   a will that leaps to obey you.
   Let all my energy blaze
   to see the joy in your face;
   let my whole being praise you,
   praise you.

Words and Music: Graham Kendrick and Steve Thompson

313 Thank you, Jesus

Chorus

Thank you, Je - sus, thank you, Je - sus,
thank you, Lord, for lov-ing me.
Thank you, Je - sus, thank you, Je -
sus, thank you, Lord, for lov-ing me.

to continue

2. You rose up from the grave,
   to me new life you gave,
   thank you, Lord, for loving me.
   You rose up from the grave,
   to me new life you gave,
   thank you, Lord, for loving me.

3. You're coming back again,
   and we with you shall reign.
   Thank you, Lord, for loving me.
   You're coming back again,
   and we with you shall reign.
   Thank you, Lord, for loving me.

Words and Music: Unknown

314 Thank you very much

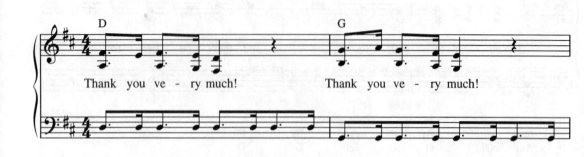

Thank you ve - ry much! Thank you ve - ry much!

Thank you ve - ry much for all you do for me! Thank you ve - ry much!

Thank you ve - ry much! Thank you ve - ry much for all you mean to me!

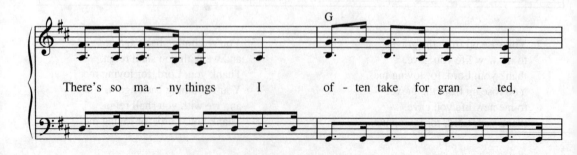

There's so ma - ny things I of - ten take for gran - ted,

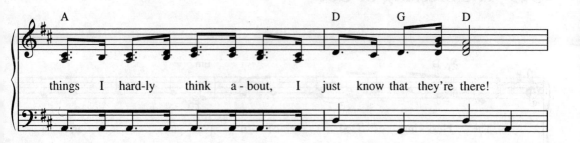

things I hard-ly think a - bout, I just know that they're there!

But I want to take the time to tell you that I'm grate - ful.

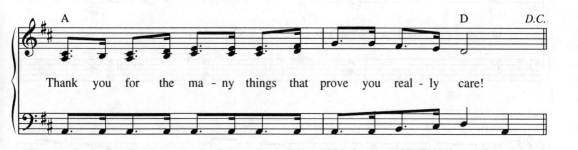

Thank you for the ma - ny things that prove you real - ly care!

Words and Music: Capt. Alan Price, CA arr. Gillian Venton

315 The blessing of God

Words and Music: John MacPherson
© Copyright 1994 J. MacPherson, 20 Megalong Road, Nedlands,
Western Australia 6009. Used by permission.

316 The gift of God is eternal life
(Jesus is the boss)

The gift of God is e-ter-nal life through Je-sus Christ, the
gift of God is e-ter-nal life through Je-sus Christ, the
gift of God is e-ter-nal life through Je-sus Christ, through
Je-sus, Je-sus Christ. Je-sus is the boss of my life,
he's the on-ly one can make it come right; Je-sus is the

Chords: Gm / Em, Dm / Bm, Gm / Em, Dm / Bm

Leader   All   Leader   All   Leader   All   Leader   All
Sound off - Je - sus, sound off - is Lord. Sound off - Je - sus, sound off - is Lord!

Chords: Gm / Em, Dm / Bm, Gm / Em, Dm Gm / Bm Em

Rap

I said, come ev'rybody and move your feet,
the rhythm is hot, it's a powerful beat.
The time is right to do some business,
get on your feet and be a witness
to the Holy One,
the King of kings, God's only Son.
Jesus Christ, that's his name,
he died to take our sin and shame.

Words and Music: Doug Horley arr. Donald Thomson

317 The joy of the Lord

The joy of the Lord is a great thing, quite dif-fer-ent from a-ny-thing I know. Je-sus in my life makes my heart sing, des-pite the things that make me feel quite low. It's a joy from deep in-side, on-ly Je-sus can pro-vide, I'm gon-na let the joy of Je-sus o-ver-flow! It's a flow!

Words and Music: Capt. Alan Price, CA

318 The promise of the Holy Spirit is for you
(Acts chapter 2, verse 39)

The pro-mise of the Ho-ly Spi-rit is for you. The pro-mise of the Ho-ly Spi-rit is for your child-ren. The pro-mise of the Ho-ly Spi-rit is for all who are far off, e-ven as ma-ny as the Lord your God shall call. Oh yeah! Acts, chap-ter two, verse thir-ty-nine. The

Words and Music: Richard Hubbard

319 The race

The race that we are run-ning may be hard, it may be tough, but in his word God pro-mised that his strength would be e - nough to see us to the fin-ish line, and there to claim the prize that Je - sus died to win for us – re - sur-rec - tion, life. We're

Words and Music: Paul Crouch and David Mudie arr. Donald Thomson

320 There are hundreds of sparrows
(Hundreds and thousands)

1. There are hun-dreds of spar-rows, thous-ands, mil-lions, they're two a pen-ny, far too ma-ny there must be; there are hun-dreds and thou-sands, mil-lions of spar-rows, but God knows ev-'ry one, and God knows me. 2. There are God knows me.

2. There are hundreds of flowers, thousands, millions,
and flowers fair the meadows wear for all to see;
there are hundreds and thousands, millions of flowers,
but God knows ev'ry one, and God knows me.

3. There are hundreds of planets, thousands, millions,
way out in space each has a place by God's decree;
there are hundreds and thousands, millions of planets,
but God knows ev'ry one, and God knows me.

4. There are hundreds of children, thousands, millions,
and yet their names are written on God's memory,
there are hundreds and thousands, millions of children,
but God knows ev'ry one, and God knows me.

Words: J. Gowans
Music: J. Leeson arr. Donald Thomson

321 There are lots of ways that I can praise

There are lots of ways that I can praise, there are ve-ry ma-ny things that
I can do; there are lots of ways that I can praise, and
show you, Lord, how much I love you. I can touch my toes,
I can hold my nose, I can crouch down low,
I can jump up high. I can clap like this, I can
do the twist, but the thing that I do best is shout, 'I love you, Lord!'

Words and Music: Steve Burnhope arr. Donald Thomson

322 There are so many stories

1. There are so ma-ny sto-ries that I love to hear, I pic-ture the scenes in my head. In books or on T - V they al - so ap-pear, I think of them all in my head. But the sto - ries of Je - sus are diff -'rent, you see, 'cos he's a real per - son who loves you and me. Though I can't see him, I know he is real;

Je - sus is my best friend. So tell me the sto - ries of

Je - sus, o - ver and o - ver and o - ver a - gain;

tell me the sto - ries of Je - sus, o - ver and o - ver a - gain. 2. There are

gain, o - ver and o - ver a - gain, o - ver and o - ver a - gain.

2. There are so many stories that I love to hear,
   I picture the scenes in my head.
   In books or on TV they also appear,
   I think of them all in my head.
   But the story of Jesus is diff'rent, I know,
   'cos he's a real person who lived long ago.
   Though he's in heaven, his Spirit is here,
   that's how he's my best friend.

Words and Music: Capt. Alan Price, CA

323 There is a God

Chorus

There is a God who knows your name, there is a God who feels your pain; there is a love holding out for you, don't turn a - way, let him love you. love you. 1. 'Cos he loves you with a pas - sion, an end - less rag - ing fire, from e -

ter - ni - ty   to   e - ter - ni - ty   you   are   his heart's de - sire.

And   if   you   could for   a   mo - ment glimpse   the

huge-ness of   his   heart,   you'd see   how he

sim - ply loves you.   There   is   a

2. He loves you with a passion, he's always on your side;
   like a mighty wave that won't be stopped,
   his love is ocean wide.
   Higher than the heavens above, and deeper than the sea;
   truth is, just this, he simply loves you.

3. When you feel you've fallen far too far to ever stand again,
   and you can't believe this Holy God could ever be your friend,
   he's shouting from the heavens above, he's there to help you through,
   you'll see how he simply loves you;
   truth is, just this, he simply loves you.

Words: Doug Horley, Belinda Horley, Penny Roberts
Music: Doug Horley arr. Donald Thomson

324 There is a place

Chorus

No one loves me like Je - sus loves me,
No one knows me like Je - sus knows me,

in his arms I'm hap - py.
no one knows like he knows.

No one loves like he

loves, he loves me.

to repeat

last time

D.S.

2. There is a me.

2. There is a secret place to go,
   where somebody knows me very well.
   There is a secret place to go
   where I can be me.
   And there my loving Jesus smiles,
   he opens his arms and welcomes me.
   There is a secret place to go
   where I can be me.

   Oh, Jesus,
   no one loves me the way you love me,
   in your arms I'm happy.
   No one knows me the way you know me,
   no one knows like you know.
   No one loves like you love,
   you love me.

Words and Music: Kath Fathers

325 There is no one else like you
(Special)

There is no one else like you, there's no one else like me.

Each of us is spe-cial to God, that's the way it's meant to be.

I'm spe-cial, you're spe-cial, we're spe-cial, don't you see,

there is no one else like you, there's no one else like me.

Black or white, short or tall, good or bad, God

loves us all. Loud or quiet, fat or thin, each of us is spe-cial to him.

Words and Music: Paul Field arr. Donald Thomson

326 There is power in the name of Jesus

Rocky

1. There is pow'r in the name of Je - sus;
we be-lieve in his name.
We have called on the name of Je - sus;
we are saved! We are saved!
At his name the de - mons flee.

At his name cap - tives are freed, for there is no o - ther name that is high - er sus! 2. There is pow'r

to verse 2

last time

2. There is pow'r in the name of Jesus,
   like a sword in our hands.
   We declare in the name of Jesus
   we shall stand! We shall stand!
   At his name God's enemies
   shall be crushed beneath our feet,
   for there is no other name that is higher
   than Jesus!

Words and Music: Noel Richards

327 There is so much to discover

1. There is so much to dis-co - ver, that God wants us to know.
There is so much to find out for our-selves, and that's the way to go.
When we learn what God has said, when we act on what we've read,
there is so much to dis-co - ver, there's so much more to know.

2. There is so much to discover,
   that God wants us to know.
   There is so much to find out for ourselves,
   and that's the way to go.
   Through the Spirit's pow'r within
   we can change the world for him.
   There is so much to discover,
   there's so much more to know.

3. There is so much to discover,
   that God wants us to know.
   There is so much to find out for ourselves,
   and that's the way to go.
   If we're ever feeling bored,
   we just need to ask the Lord
   to show to us the things he's planned for us to do,
   and that's the way to go.

Words and Music: Capt. Alan Price, CA

328 There, on a cruel cross

1. There, on a cru-el cross, for all to see; killed like a cri-mi-nal, how could it be? That Je-sus bore such pain and shame, mocked by those who on-ly came to stand and watch, yet still not see what God was do-ing then, for you and me.

Lord,

I may ne-ver un-der-stand, or know the rea-son why the

on-ly way to be for-giv'n was that you should die;

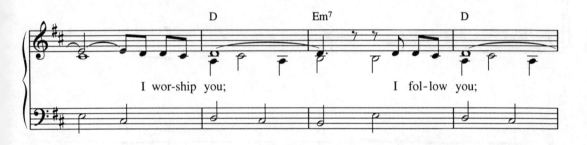

I wor-ship you; I fol-low you;

I live for you; I trust in you.

2. There, on a cruel cross, so painfully;
   killed like a criminal, yet willingly.
   Lord Jesus bore such pain and shame,
   for that is why he really came;
   the greatest act of history,
   what God was doing then,
   for you and me.

Words and Music: Capt. Alan Price, CA

329 There once was a man called Daniel
(Good old Daniel)

There once was a man called Dan - iel (good old Dan - iel), and

Dan - iel prayed three times a day (good old Dan - iel); but the

King's dec - ree said 'Wor - ship me!' (poor old Dan - iel), but

Dan - iel would not bend the knee! (good old Dan - iel). So the

Words and Music: Unknown

330 There's a King above the heavens
(King of Heaven)

1. There's a King a-bove the hea - vens, there's a King a-bove the earth, and from out of time - less his - to - ry, he brought man-kind to birth. And when sin brought se-pa-ra - tion, and tore the heart of the King, he sent his son, Je - sus Christ, a sac - ri - fice for sin. Hoop sah oh, oh, oh. Hoop sah oh, oh, oh. Hoop sa oh.

Words and Music: Doug Horley and Vanessa Freeman arr. Donald Thomson

331 There's nothing better

Words and Music: Ian Smale

332 There's nothing I like better than to praise

Words and Music: Ian Smale

333 There were ninety-nine sheep
(Lost and found)

There were nine-ty-nine sheep back safe in the fold, but one of them's left out-side in the cold. The shep-herd was wond-'ring, 'Oh, where, tell me where can it be? Can it be? Where? Where? Where's the mis-sing one? Where? Where?

Where's the mis-sing one? Oh, where can it be?'

2. So the shepherd set out in dead of the night,
   the wind and the rain, a pitiful sight.
   He kept right on searching,
   but no sheep at all could he see!
   Could he see!
   Where? Where? Where's the missing one?
   Where? Where? Where's the missing one?
   Oh, where can it be?

3. But the shepherd, at last, he found his lost sheep,
   all ragged and cold and trying to sleep.
   He picked it right up
   and he carried it home. Now it's found!
   Now it's found!
   There! There! There's the missing one!
   There! There! There's the missing one!
   And now it is found!

Words and Music: Roger Jones arr. Donald Thomson

334 The Spirit lives to set us free
(Walk in the light)

1. The Spi-rit lives to set us free, walk, walk in the light. He binds us all in u-ni-ty, walk, walk in the light. Walk in the light, walk in the light, walk in the light, walk in the light of the Lord. Lord.

2. Jesus promised life to all,
   walk, walk in the light.
   The dead were wakened by his call,
   walk, walk in the light.

3. He died in pain on Calvary,
   walk, walk in the light,
   to save the lost like you and me,
   walk, walk in the light.

4. We know his death was not the end,
   walk, walk in the light.
   He gave his Spirit to be our friend,
   walk, walk in the light.

5. The Spirit lives in you and me,
   walk, walk in the light.
   His light will shine for all to see,
   walk, walk in the light.

Words: Damian Lundy
Music: Unknown arr. Noel Rawsthorne
© Copyright 1978 Kevin Mayhew Ltd.

335 The time has come

Joyfully

Verse 𝄋 G ... D

1. The time has come to have some fun, don't stand a-lone, get with some-one. We're

Em ... C ... G

gon-na have a par-ty in this place. Let the mu-sic fill the air, let

D ... Em

joy and laugh-ter lift your cares. We're gon-na have a par-ty in this

C ... Am ... A ... D

place, we're gon-na have a par-ty in this place.

Chorus

C ... D ... G ... D ... G

Time to be hap-py, let me hear you shout:

© Copyright 1995 Kingsway's Thankyou Music, P.O. Box 75, Eastbourne,
East Sussex, BN23 6NW, UK. Used by permission.

danc - ing with friends, let your joy break out.

Je - sus is a-mongst us, he loves to see you smile.

Leave your sad - ness and be hap - py for a while,

hap - py for a while. while.

2. Wave the banners, ribbons too:
   God wants his joy to flow through you.
   We're gonna have a party in this place.
   Don't hold back or live in fear,
   there's room for young and old ones here,
   we're gonna have a party in this place,
   we're gonna have a party in this place.

Words and Music: Mick Gisbey

336 The wise man built his house upon the rock

1. The wise man built his house upon the rock, the wise man built his house up-on the rock, the wise man built his house up-on the rock, and the rain came tum-bling down. And the rain came down and the floods came up, the rain came down and the floods came up, the rain came down and the floods came up, and the house on the rock stood firm.

2. The foolish man built his house upon the sand, (x3)
and the rain came tumbling down.
(And) the rain came down and the floods came up, (x3)
and the house on the sand fell flat.

Words and Music: Unknown arr. Donald Thomson
This arrangement © Copyright 1999 Kevin Mayhew Ltd.

337 The women went to Jesus' tomb
(Roll the stone away)

2. They found that Jesus was alive,
   and still he lives today,
   for God has raised him from the dead,
   and rolled the stone away.

3. Don't let your heart be like a tomb,
   empty, dark and grey.
   Trust in Jesus, he's the rock
   to roll your stone away.

Chorus after v.3
Roll the stone, roll the stone,
roll the stone away.
Trust in Jesus, he's the rock
to roll your stone away.
Trust in Jesus, he's the rock
to roll your stone away.

Words and Music: Paul Field

338 The word of the Lord is planted in my heart
(The sower song)

The word of the Lord is plan-ted in my heart and I want to see it grow. The word of the Lord is plan-ted in my heart and I want you to know, I won't let the e-ne-my take it, or let bad times shake it; I won't let o-ther things choke it out (choke, choke, choke), 'cos I want to let it grow, grow, grow, 'cos I want to let it grow! (yeah!)

(last time)

Words and Music: Capt. Alan Price, CA

339 This is a catchy songa
(The Christian conga)

This is a cat-chy song-a, we sing it to the cong-a, we

dance and sing to Christ the King. Why don't you sing a-long-a,

while we dance the cong-a, praise God a-bove for all his love.

Verses (spoken)

1. King David danced before the Lord,
   worship filled his heart;
   we can dance before him, too,
   this is how we start . . .

2. Jesus is the greatest friend,
   alive for us today,
   he said, 'I'm with you 'till the end,
   I'm with you all the way!' . . .

Words: Capt. Alan Price, CA
Music: Traditional
Words © Copyright 1990 Daybreak Music Ltd, Silverdale Road, Eastbourne,
East Sussex, BN20 7AB, UK. Used by permission.

340 This is a song for the children of the Lord

1. This is a song for the chil-dren of the Lord, a sim-ple song to our King. A song of hap-pi-ness and sim-ple faith, our praise and thanks we bring.

2. This is a dance for the children of the Lord,
a simple dance for our King.
A dance of happiness and simple faith,
our praise and thanks we bring.

3. Lai, lai, lai . . .

Words and Music: Capt. Alan Price, CA arr. Gillian Venton
© Copyright 1996 Daybreak Music Ltd, Silverdale Road, Eastbourne,
East Sussex, BN20 7AB, UK. Used by permission.

341 This is the day

Brightly, with pace

This is the day, this is the day that the Lord has made, that the Lord has made; we shall re-joice, we shall re-joice and be glad in it, and be glad in it. This is the day that the Lord has made, we shall re-joice and be glad in it; this is the day, this is the day that the Lord has made.

Words and Music: Les Garrett

342 This is the nose God chose for me

Verse

1. This is the nose God chose for me, and I sup-pose that you can see, there's no one in the world with a nose like me, thank you, Lord.

Chorus

Thank you, Lord, be-cause we know it's true, all these diff-'rent fa-ces, look beau-ti-ful to you.

2. These are the ears God chose for me,
   and I suppose that you can see,
   there's no one in the world with ears like me,
   thank you, Lord.

3. This is the mouth God chose for me,
   and I suppose that you can see,
   there's no one in the world with a mouth like me,
   thank you, Lord.

4. These are the eyes God chose for me,
   and I suppose that you can see,
   there's no one in the world with eyes like me,
   thank you, Lord.

Words and Music: Paul Field

343 This little light of mine

This lit-tle light of mine, I'm gon-na let it shine.

This lit-tle light of mine, I'm gon-na let it shine.

This lit-tle light of mine, I'm gon-na let it shine. Ev-'ry day,

ev-'ry day, ev-'ry day in ev-'ry way. I'm gon-na

let my lit-tle light shine. On a Mon-day, he gave me the gift

Words and Music: Ernie Rettino and Debbie Kerner Rettino

344 Three little words that mean so much
(God loves me)

1. Three lit-tle words that mean so much, 'God loves me!' Three lit-tle words that deep-ly touch me, 'God loves me!' I know it, 'cos God said it, and he would ne-ver lie. I know it, 'cos he showed it, when he sent his Son to

die for me. Three lit-tle words that mean so much,

'God loves me!'

1. D

2. D you!'

2. Three little words I mean so much, Lord,
   'I love you!'
   Three little words I want to tell you,
   'I love you!'
   You know that when I say it,
   I'm trying to be real.
   You know that when I say it,
   it's not just when I feel you love me.
   Three little words I want to tell you,
   'I love you!'

Words and Music: Capt. Alan Price, CA arr. Donald Thomson

345 Two little eyes

Two lit-tle eyes to look to God, two lit-tle ears to
hear his word, two lit-tle feet to walk in his ways,
two lit-tle lips to sing his praise. Two lit-tle hands to
do his will, and one lit-tle heart to love him still.

Words and Music: C. C. Kerr arr. Donald Thomson

346 Uh well, it's excellent to be obedient
(It's excellent to be obedient)

Chorus

Uh well, it's ex - cel - lent to be o - be - di - ent, u – hu – hu!

Uh well, it's ex - cel - lent to be o -

be - di - ent, u – hu – hu! You don't say 'no' to your

ma and pa; you say, 'u – hu'.

Verse

1. Uh well, it ain't real good to be real rude, no, no, no.

Uh well, it ain't real good to be real rude, no, no, no.

You've got - ta treat your pa - rents like you

know you should, u – hu – hu!

2. It don't show aptitude to have an attitude,
   no, no, no.
   It don't show aptitude to have an attitude,
   no, no, no.
   You've gotta treat your parents like you know you should,
   u-hu-hu!

Words and Music: Sammy Horner arr. Donald Thomson

347 Up, down, turn around
(Fit for life)

Up, down, turn a-round, touch your head, touch the ground,

left, right, side to side, legs to-ge-ther, legs a-stride,

stand up straight, touch your toes, squeeze your tum, pinch your nose.

Up, down, turn a-round, clap your hands and shout (all right!)

Fit for life, in bo-dy and in mind. Fit for life, to

live for Je-sus all the time. Up, down, turn a-round, clap your hands and shout (yeah!)

Words and Music: Paul Field

348 Up, up, up and away

Chorus G
Up, up, up and a-way! We're tak-ing off as we fol-low Je - sus.

G ... Bm C D G *Fine*
Up, up, up and a-way! We're mov-ing on with God.

Verse C ... G ... D
1. Our lug-gage packed and our tic-ket in hand, we come to Je - sus and we

G ... C ... G
un-der-stand that he paid a great price, e-ven will-ing to die. When we

A ... D *D.C.*
know we're for-gi - ven it's as if we can fly!

2. His Spirit's fuel gives the power we need
   for ev'ry word, and for ev'ry deed,
   and a beacon is there to guide us along,
   his word is the Bible, shows what's right and what's wrong.

Words and Music: Capt. Alan Price, CA arr. Gillian Venton
© Copyright 1996 Daybreak Music Ltd, Silverdale Road, Eastbourne,
East Sussex, BN20 7AB, UK. Used by permission.

349 We are kingdom kids

We are king - dom kids, kids of the king-dom.

We let Je - sus Christ be num-ber one in our

lives. We are king - dom kids, kids of the king-dom.

We're gon-na serve our God and King.

verse 1

1. Je - sus Christ is a - live, reign-ing with the Fa - ther,

Words and Music: Jim Bailey

350 We are marching
(Siyahamba)

2. We are living in the love of God . . .

3. We are moving in the pow'r of God . . .

Words and Music: Traditional South African

Translation: (vs.1) Anders Nyberg; (vs.2 & 3) Andrew Maries

351 We are one, we are family

We are one, we are fa-mi-ly to-ge-ther,
'cause we've one Fa-ther ca-ring for us all.
We are one, we are re-la-ted to each o-ther;
Lord, help me to love my fa-mi-ly much more.

Words and Music: Ian Smale arr. Donald Thomson
© Copyright 1982 Kingsway's Thankyou Music, P.O. Box 75, Eastbourne,
East Sussex, BN23 6NW, UK. Used by permission.

352 We are the Lord's kids
(March of the kids)

We are the Lord's kids, his kids, spe - cial kids, cho - sen kids,

big kids, lit - tle kids, fol - low-ing the Lord. We are the

Lord's kids, his kids, spe - cial kids, cho - sen kids,

big kids, lit - tle kids, fol - low-ing the Lord!

Verse

1. Though we may be small, Je - sus wants us all; an

ar - my for the Lord, liv - ing by his Word.

Though we may be small, Je - sus wants us all; an

ar - my for the Lord, liv - ing by his Word.

We are the

2. However old we are,
   we can know his pow'r;
   whoever we may be,
   Jesus is the key. *(Repeat)*

3. The way we think, the way we act,
   the enemy we'll fight!
   At school, at home, at work, at play,
   we'll learn to do what's right. *(Repeat)*

Words and Music: Capt. Alan Price, CA arr. D. Coad

353 We believe in Hebrews 13:8

We be-lieve in He-brews thir-teen, eight,
Je-sus Christ is ne-ver out of date. If it's
yes-ter-day or to-day, or for e-ver-more,
Je-sus stays the same and that is great.

Words and Music: Ian Smale

354 We don't believe the devil's lie
(SWAT march)

U.S. Army marching style

1. We don't be-lieve the de-vil's lie, we will shout our bat-tle cry. Though we may be ve-ry small, Je-sus Christ is Lord of all. He's good for me, he's good for you. He's

good for me,   good for our whole church.

Je-sus' name   our vic-to-ry.   go a-way,   in

Je-sus' name!   Now go a-way,   in Je-sus' name.

2. When temptation comes our way,
   this is what we're gonna say:
   'Don't you come and mess with me,
   in Jesus' name our victory.
   In Jesus' name our victory.
   In Jesus' name our victory.'

3. Jesus is the King of kings,
   he's the Lord of ev'rything.
   If Satan comes, here's what we say:
   'In Jesus' name, now go away.
   Now go away, in Jesus' name!
   Now go away, in Jesus' name!
   Now go away, in Jesus' name!'

Words and Music: Sammy Horner

355 We don't sing songs

1. We don't sing songs just for our-selves, we sing them for our King, and if we real-ly mean it, then he loves it when we sing. So we clap our hands (clap), stamp our feet (stamp), jump up and down (boing, boing), touch our toes (oh!), and sing them for our King, sing them for our King, sing them for our King, sing them for our King.

2. We don't sing songs to please our friends,
   we sing them for our King,
   and if we really mean it,
   then he loves it when we sing.
   So we . . .

The 'clap our hands' part of the song may be repeated using different actions.

Words and Music: Paul Crouch and David Mudie

356 Welcome

1. Wel - come, wel - come, we're glad that you have come;
wel - come, wel - come, from each and ev - 'ry one.

2. Welcome, welcome,
   we're glad that you belong;
   welcome, welcome,
   from each and ev'ry one.

Words: Geoffrey Gardner
Music: Douglas Coombes
© Copyright Geoffrey Gardner. Used by permission.

357 Welcome to the family

Words and Music: Debby Kerner

358 We'll sing this song for you
(Birthday song)

We'll sing this song for you, a birth-day song for you, we'll sing this song for you to-day. May Je-sus be with you in ev-'ry-thing you do, this is our birth-day pray'r for you to-day.

Hap-py birth-day! Hap-py birth-day! Hap-py birth-day to you!

Words and Music: Capt. Alan Price, CA arr. Gillian Venton

359 We need to grow

Words and Music: Capt. Alan Price, CA

360 We praise God

1. We praise God in the morn-ing when the sun is bright, we
praise him in the eve-ning when day turns to night. We
praise him if it's sun-ny or if it's wet. No
mat-ter what the wea-ther we'll ne-ver for-get to praise God (bop, bop, sho-
wad-dy do wah). Praise God (bop, bop, sho-wad-dy do wah). Hal-le-

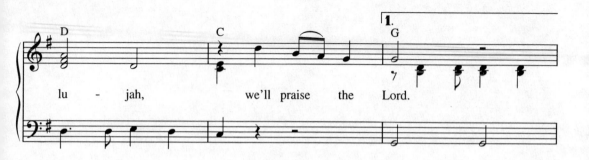

lu - jah, we'll praise the Lord.

last time

2. We Lord.

2. We praise God when we're singing our songs of praise,
   we praise him when we worship in our different ways.
   We praise him for the food that we eat each day
   but in ev'rything we do we want to say . . .

Words and Music: Capt. Alan Price, CA

361 We praise you, Jesus

We praise you, Je - sus, we praise you, Je - sus, we just want to let you know. We praise you, Je - sus, we praise you, Je - sus, when you came so long a - go. You came to save us, new life you gave us, when you died up - on the cross. And that's the rea - son that we're be -liev - in' that you real - ly care for us!

Words and Music: Capt. Alan Price, CA

© Copyright 1990 Daybreak Music, Silverdale Road, Eastbourne,
East Sussex, BN20 7AB, UK. Used by permission.

362 We're a bright light together

We're a bright light to-ge-ther, with the light of Je - sus we shine; we're a grand band to - ge -ther, with our friend Je - sus it's fine. We're a swell smell to - ge-ther, it's the fra-grance of Je - sus we share! When-e - ver we are to - ge-ther, Je -sus is spe - cial-ly

Words and Music: Capt. Alan Price, CA arr. B. Chesser

363 We're going to praise the Lord

praise him in more nor-mal ways (hal - le-lu-jah! hal - le-lu); we'll

praise him by the way we live (stand up, stand up for Je - sus); we'll

praise him in the way we give (time and money, time and money).

More than a-ny-thing else we do, Lord, we give our praise to you!

Words and Music: Capt. Alan Price, CA

364 We wanna sing about your love

1. We wan-na sing a-bout your love and tell ev-'ry-one we know. Let it change our lives so that we can let it show. Fa-ther, we re-ceive your love that comes from know - ing you, as we en - joy your love, help us show love to o - thers too. Let your love pour in - to our lives, O Lord, let your love pour in - to our lives.

Let your love pour in-to our lives, O Lord, let your

love pour in-to our lives. 2. We wan-na

2. We wanna sing about your love
   and tell ev'ryone we know.
   Let it change our lives
   so that we can let it show.
   Jesus, we receive the joy
   that comes from knowing you.
   The way you gave your life,
   help us to offer ours to you.
   Let your joy pour into our lives . . .

3. We wanna sing about your love
   and tell ev'ryone we know.
   Let it change our lives
   so that we can let it show.
   Spirit, we receive the pow'r
   that comes from knowing you.
   Will you change our lives,
   so we can be of use to you?
   Let your pow'r pour into our lives . . .

Words and Music: Andrew and Pauline Pearson arr. Donald Thomson

365 We want to see Jesus lifted high

We want to see Je - sus lift - ed high,
a ban - ner that flies a - cross this land,
that all men might see the truth and know
he is the way to hea - ven.

We want to see, / (We're gon-na)
we want to see, / (we're gon-na)
we want to see Je - sus lift - ed high. / (we're gon-na)

Words and Music: Doug Horley

366 We will turn the hearts

2. The walls have been broken, we stand as one now,
   one in the Spirit and won by your blood.
   We're moving forwards under your banner,
   telling the world of your glory.
   And we take on your promise,
   together we'll welcome the Day of the Lord!

Words and Music: Kath Hall

367 We worship you

2. I don't pretend to understand
   how this can really be,
   yet by faith I know it's true,
   this holy mystery.

Words and Music: Capt. Alan Price, CA

368 What a whale of a tale
(Jonah song)

What a whale of a tale when Jo - nah sailed out on the o - cean blue: God spoke that day, but he ran a - way from what he was told to do; and out on a boat that could hard - ly float, on a rough and stor - my sea, the sail - ors asked: 'Whose fault is this?' And Jo - nah piped up: 'Me!'

Words and Music: Mick Gisbey

369 What noise shall we make

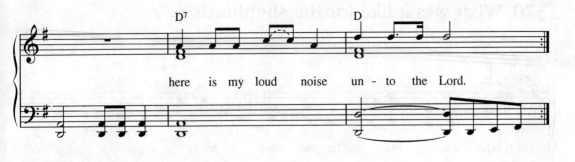

here is my loud noise un - to the Lord.

last time

(All)
We love mak - ing noise to say that God is great.

We love mak - ing noise un - to the Lord.

2. Let's make a quiet noise . . .
   Here is my quiet noise: . . .

3. Let's make a fast noise . . .
   Here is my fast noise: . . .

4. Let's make a slow noise . . .
   Here is my slow noise: . . .

5. Let's make a joyful noise . . .
   Here is my joyful noise: . . .

6. Let's make a praising noise . . .
   Here is my praising noise: God is good! . . .

   We love making noise
   to say that God is great.
   We love making noise
   unto the Lord.

Words and Music: Lucy East

370 What was it like for the shepherds

1. What was it like for the shepherds, out on the hills in the night? What was it like for the shepherds, on see-ing the bright shin-ing light? Hear the an - gels! Glo - ry! Glo - ry! Glo - ry to God on high!

2. What was it like for the shepherds,
   seeing an angel out there?
   What was it like for the shepherds,
   so scared by the sudden bright glare?

3. What was it like for the shepherds,
   leaving their sheep in the cold?
   What was it like for the shepherds,
   to do as the angel had told?

4. There was great joy for the shepherds,
   leaving their fields cold and wild!
   There was great joy for the shepherds
   on seeing the newly born child.

Words: Mary Wright
Music: Roger Jones arr. Donald Thomson

371 When a knight won his spurs

STOWEY 12 12 12 12

1. When a knight won his spurs, in the sto-ries of old, he was gen-tle and brave, he was gal-lant and bold; with a shield on his arm and a lance in his hand, for God and for val-our he rode through the land.

2. No charger have I, and no sword by my side,
   yet still to adventure and battle I ride,
   though back into storyland giants have fled,
   and the knights are no more and the dragons are dead.

3. Let faith be my shield and let joy be my steed
   'gainst the dragons of anger, the ogres of greed;
   and let me set free, with the sword of my youth,
   for the castle of darkness, the pow'r of the truth.

Words: Jan Struther
Music: Traditional English arr. Donald Thomson

372 Whenever I'm afraid

Words and Music: Capt. Alan Price, CA

373 When I am hurt

1. When I am hurt in the dai-ly fight to live for Je-sus and do what is right, I'll find a qui-et place, and then I'll pray and ask God to heal what's been dam-aged that day. I'll way.

2. I'll ask his forgiveness for things I've done wrong,
   and breathe in his Spirit once more to be strong;
   and so I'll be ready to face a new day,
   with ev'ry new challenge that may come my way.

Words and Music: Capt. Alan Price, CA arr. Donald Thomson
© Copyright 1998 Daybreak Music Ltd, Silverdale Road, Eastbourne,
East Sussex, BN20 7AB, UK. Used by permission.

374 When I look at the trees
(God's wonderful world)

2. When I feel the gentle rain,
   splashing down again,
   oo, I praise you, oo, I praise you.
   When I touch the golden sand,
   spreading it with my hand,
   oo, I praise you, oo, I praise you.

3. When I see the silver stars,
   sparkling in the skies,
   oo, I praise you, oo, I praise you.

Words: Rosie Jarvis
Music: Julia Plaut arr. Donald Thomson

375 When I'm in bed and it's night
(I've got a friend)

1. When I'm in bed and it's night, I don't want mum to turn out the light be-cause there might be gi-ants or things that frigh-ten, or mon-sters look-ing at me. But when I'm shak-

When-e-ver I call you, you're al-rea-dy here, and you al-ways lis-ten what-e-ver my fear, and I want to know you more and now I'm sure that friends for-e-ver we'll be. 2. There's a

2. There's a boy in the class above me,
   and he's so much bigger than me,
   and I don't want to go to the playground,
   'cause I am scared of what he'd do to me.

   But I've got a friend . . .

3. And when I'm feeling sad and alone,
   and all the other kids have gone home,
   then I can pray and call out your name
   and I'll know that you are with me once more.

   And I've got a friend . . .

Words and Music: Dave Bird and Sarah Lacy

376 When I think about the cross

Words and Music: Mark and Helen Johnson arr. Donald Thomson
© Copyright Out of the Ark Music. Administered by Daybreak Music, Silverdale Road,
Eastbourne, East Sussex, BN20 7AB, UK. Used by permission.

377 When there is nowhere to turn

When there is no-where to turn, when there is no-one who cares, when I am feel-ing a-fraid and a-lone, my Je-sus will al-ways be there. I know I'm his pre-cious child. I know he's my spe-cial friend. I know that I'll al-ways be safe in his love, as I give him my heart once a-gain.

Words and Music: Nigel Hemming arr. Donald Thomson

378 When there's hard times
(Come what may)

1. When there's hard times or there's good times, when the
rain falls or the sun shines, when you test me or you
bless me my re-solve will none the less be: I will
love you come what may, I will love you ev-'ry day; I will
love you now and for e-ver-more.

2. When there's

2. When there's dark clouds or there's clear skies,
   when it's sunset or it's sunrise,
   when I'm needy or I've plenty,
   Lord, not one thing will prevent me:

3. When your presence seems so distant,
   when my doubts seem so persistent,
   then no matter how I'm feeling,
   Lord, in one thing I'm unyielding:

4. When the battle seems so endless,
   when I'm feeling so defenceless,
   when the enemy surrounds me
   and his arrows fly around me:

5. When my future is uncertain,
   when my heart is heavy-burdened,
   when I'm tired or I'm hurting,
   Lord, in one thing I'm determined:

6. When the past seems to pursue me,
   when temptation whispers to me,
   when my worst fears are awakened,
   Lord, on one thing I'm unshaken:

Words and Music: Joe King

379 When the time is right

When the time is right, whe-ther day or night, the Lord Je-sus Christ will come a-gain (he'll come a-gain). As we wait for that day, in our work and our play, we'll let our light shine bright and live for the King who will reign. When the time is right,

Words and Music: Capt. Alan Price, CA
© Copyright 1994 Daybreak Music, Silverdale Road, Eastbourne,
East Sussex, BN20 7AB, UK. Used by permission.

380 When we're together with Jesus

When we're to-ge-ther with Je-sus and we hap-pi-ly sing his songs, it's ea-sy to be his fol-low-er, it's good to know we be-long; but at o-ther times it can be so hard to do what's right and good. When those a-round don't know the Lord, and don't live as they should.

O Lord, keep me strong, ne-ver to de-ny you. O Lord, when it's hard, help me to keep by you.

Words and Music: Capt. Alan Price, CA

381 When you pray

Words and Music: Mike Burn

382 When you're feeling good
(Thumbs up)

Words and Music: Paul Field and Ralph Chambers

383 Wherever he rules

Words and Music: Capt. Alan Price, CA arr. Donald Thomson

384 Whether you're one

2. Whether you're big or whether you're small,
   or somewhere in between,
   first in the class or middle or last,
   we're all the same to him.
   It really doesn't matter how clever you are,
   Jesus loves you whoever you are.

Words and Music: Graham Kendrick

385 Who made the twinkling stars

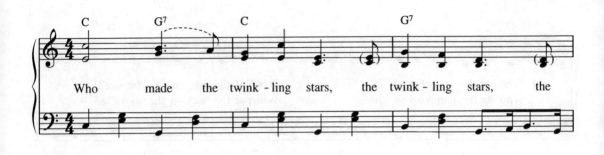

Who made the twink-ling stars, the twink-ling stars, the

twink-ling stars? Who made the twink-ling stars?

to repeat Our Fa - ther God. *last time* God.

2. Who made the birds that fly,
   the birds that fly, the birds that fly?
   Who made the birds that fly?
   Our Father God.

3. Who made the rolling seas,
   the rolling seas, the rolling seas?
   Who made the rolling seas?
   Our Father God.

4. Who made you and me,
   you and me, you and me?
   Who made you and me?
   Our Father God.

Words and Music: Unknown, arr. Donald Thomson

386 Who put the colours in the rainbow?

1. Who put the co-lours in the rain - bow? Who put the salt in-to the sea?
Who put the hump up-on the ca - mel? Who put the neck on the gi-raffe?

Who put the cold in-to the snow-flake? Who made you and me?
Who put the tail up-on the mon - key? Who made hy-e - nas laugh?

Who made whales and snails and quails? Who made hogs and dogs and frogs?

Who made bats and rats and cats? Who made ev - 'ry - thing?

2. Who put the gold into the sunshine?
Who put the sparkle in the stars?
Who put the silver in the moonlight?
Who made Earth and Mars?
Who put the scent into the roses?
Who taught the honey bees to dance?
Who put the tree inside the acorn?
It surely can't be chance!
Who made seas and leaves and trees?
Who made snow and winds that blow?
Who made streams and rivers flow?
God made all of these!

Words and Music: Paul Booth arr. Noel Rawsthorne

387 Who spoke words of wisdom and life?

2. Who took children into his arms?
   Only the one they call Jesus.
   Spoke to storms and made them calm?
   Nobody other than him.
   Who raised Lazarus from the dead?
   Only the one they call Jesus.
   Made a feast of fishes and bread?
   Nobody other than him.

3. Who made friends with people despised?
   Only the one they call Jesus.
   Turned the water into good wine?
   Nobody other than him.
   Who got people following him?
   Only the one they call Jesus.
   Changed their lives, forgave all their sin?
   Nobody other than him.

Words and Music: Mark and Helen Johnson

388 Who's the king of the jungle?

Words and Music: Unknown arr. Noel Rawsthorne

389 Who taught the spider
(My Father)

In calypso style

Verse

1. Who taught the spi-der to spin his web? Who spoke the first words e-ver said? Who put the waves in the deep blue sea? Who knows all there is a-bout me, me, me? My Fa-ther.

Chorus

My Fa-ther is big, he's strong and he's tough. I know that he cares, his word I trust, When-

e - ver I fall, he helps me to stand. My Fa - ther holds me se -

cure in his hand.

2. Who taught the bird to sing her song?
   Who drew the line between right and wrong?
   Who paints the rainbow across the sky?
   Who will hear me when I cry, cry, cry?
   My Father.

   Chorus twice to end

Words and Music: Paul Herbert arr. Donald Thomson

390 Why is it me?

Chorus

Why is it me? Why is it me? Why do all the things like this hap-pen to me? Why is it me? Why is it me? Is-n't there some - one else o - ther than me?

Verse

1. A - na - ni - as heard the Lord call him one day, 'I've got a job for you to do straight a - way. Find a house in Straight St. and

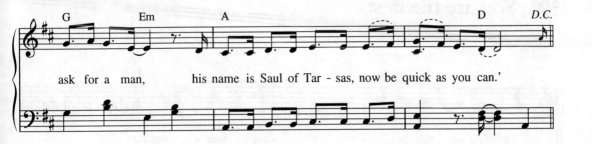

ask for a man, his name is Saul of Tar - sas, now be quick as you can.'

2. 'This Saul had a vision and it's going to come true,
   he's seen a man lay hands on him, and that man is you!'
   Ananias was worried, 'cos he'd heard about Saul,
   he'd caused trouble for believers – he wasn't nice at all! Oh . . .

3. God said, 'Go, Ananias, and do what I ask,
   I've chosen this Saul for a special task.'
   Ananias knew that he had to obey,
   he knew that he could trust the Lord, come what may. But . . .

4. He went and found the house and laid his hands on Saul,
   the Holy spirit came with power – it didn't hurt at all.
   God asks hard things even now – and of children too.
   Don't miss the adventure, it could happen to you! Oh . . .

last chorus
   Could it be me? Could it be me?
   How could anything like this happen to me?
   Could it be me? Could it be me?
   Though there may be someone else, it could be me.

Words and Music: Capt. Alan Price, CA

391 You are the best

392 You are the Light of the world

1. You are the Light of the world.
I won't walk in darkness.
You are the Way, the Truth and the Life, I'm gonna follow you.

You are the great I AM, who was and is and is to come.

2. You are the Good Shepherd,
   you take care of me.
   You are the Resurrection and the Life,
   I'm gonna live with you.

3. You are the Bread of Life,
   I will not be hungry.
   You are the Vine and I am the branch,
   I will abide in you.

Words and Music: Chris Jackson
© Copyright 1998 Powerpack/Learning Curve Music, P.O. Box 421, Hailsham,
East Sussex, BN27 4ZA, UK. Used by permission.

393 You can't catch a plane
(Only Jesus)

Words: Ralph Chambers
Music: Paul Field

394 You give me joy

2. I want to laugh and clap my hands,
   I want to praise you through the land,
   'cos you give me joy, such a bubbly joy
   that no one else can give me.

Words and Music: Bev Gammon

395 You lift your left arm high
(Holy Hokey)

Verse

1. You lift your left arm high, your left arm high, your left arm straight up, wave it in the sky. You raise your arm to Je-sus as you sing God's praise, it's the Ho-ly Ho-key for God!

Chorus

Give the glo-ry to the Fa-ther, give the glo-ry to the Son, give the glo-ry to the Spi-rit, our

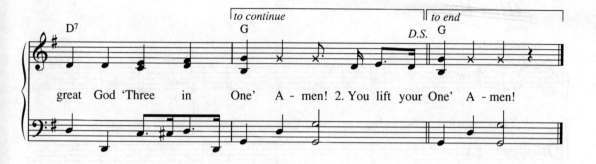

to continue

to end

great God 'Three in One' A - men! 2. You lift your One' A - men!

2. You lift your right arm high, your right arm high,
   your right arm straight up, wave it in the sky.
   You raise your arm to Jesus as you sing God's praise,
   it's the Holy Hokey for God!

3. You lift your left arm high, your right arm high,
   both arms straight up, wave them in the sky.
   You raise your arms to Jesus as you sing God's praise,
   it's the Holy Hokey for God!

4. You lift your face up high, your face up high,
   lift your face up, gazing to the sky.
   You're looking up to Jesus as you sing God's praise,
   it's the Holy Hokey for God!

Words and Music: Capt. Alan Price, CA arr. Donald Thomson

396 You may be happy, you may be sad
(Just the same)

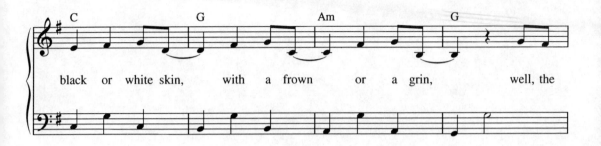

black or white skin, with a frown or a grin, well, the

Lord loves us all just the same. 3. They

2. You may be wealthy, you may be poor,
   you may be scruffy or smart;
   but love is real when you know for sure,
   it takes you just as you are.

3. They say to copy the TV stars,
   they say 'keep up with the trends';
   to have the fashions and look the part,
   just like the rest of your friends.

4. They say 'Try harder', they say 'Perform',
   they say 'Do things to impress';
   but love is real when you know for sure,
   it won't depend on success.

Chorus twice to end

Words and Music: Mark and Helen Johnson

397 You may think I'm so young
(The grasshopper song)

You may think I'm so young, too young to un-der-stand; don't for-get, in God's eyes, he looks on me as grand. He ne-ver, ne-ver li-mits the gi-ant that's in me; he leads me through my child-hood, su-per-nat-'ral-ly.

I'm not a grass-hop-per, I'm a gi-ant in the Lord.

I'm not a grass-hop-per, I'm a gi-ant in the Lord.

Words and Music: Mick Gisbey

398 You never put a light under a dirty old bucket

Words and Music: Ian Smale

399 Your name is Jesus

Words and Music: Ian White

400 You say the harvest is plentiful
(Ready and willing)

2. I'll stay here in my street,
I'll tell the people I meet,
about Lord Jesus Christ,
who set me free inside.

3. I'll go to Africa,
I'll go to India,
wherever you send me,
that's where I want to be.

Words and Music: Ian White

© Copyright 1987 Little Misty Music. Administered by Kingsway's Thankyou Music, P.O. Box 75, Eastbourne,
East Sussex, BN23 6NW, UK. Worldwide (excl. Australia & New Zealand). Used by permission.

Indexes

Index of Songwriters, Authors, Composers and Arrangers

Scriptural Index

Key Word Index

*The key word categories appear alphabetically and are cross-referenced to make it as easy as possible
for worship leaders to find songs and hymns suitable for various themes and occasions.*

ASCENSION

See **Jesus – Ascension**

BIBLE

BIBLE STORIES/PASSAGES

BIRTHDAY

CALL TO WORSHIP

CELEBRATION

CHRISTINGLE

CHRISTMAS

Index of First Lines and Titles

This index gives the first line of each hymn. If a hymn is known by an
alternative title, this is also given, but indented and in italics.